HOLT

Elements of

Language

THIRD COURSE

Chapter Tests

- Reading
- Writing
- Sentences and Paragraphs
- Grammar, Usage, Mechanics

HOLT, RINEHART AND WINSTON

A Harcourt Education Company

Orlando • **Austin** • New York • San Diego • London

ISBN 978-0-03-099155-4

ISBN 0-03-099155-2

1 2 3 4 5 6   018   13 12 11 10 09 08 07

Table of Contents

Table of Contents

Communications

About These Tests

Every chapter in your *Elements of Language* Student Edition has an accompanying Chapter Test in traditional format. The Answer Keys for these tests are located on the *Teacher One Stop*.

Part 1   **Grammar, Usage, and Mechanics**

The Part 1 tests provide assessment for the rules and key concepts taught in the grammar, usage, and mechanics chapters in the Student Edition. Students demonstrate their mastery of the instruction by completing a variety of tests that are similar to the exercises in the Student Edition.

Part 2   **Sentences and Paragraphs**

The Part 2 tests provide assessment for each major section within the Sentences and Paragraphs chapters. Students complete exercises similar to those in the Student Edition. These exercises test students' mastery of the key concepts taught in the chapters.

Part 3   **Communications**

The Part 3 tests include assessment for both the Reading and the Writing Workshops. You may choose to administer the Reading and Writing Workshop tests separately or as one test after students have completed the chapter.

In the **Reading Workshop** test, students read a passage, respond to short-answer questions, and complete a graphic organizer. The passage is in the mode that students have just studied, and the questions and the graphic organizer assess students' proficiency in the chapter's Reading Skill and Reading Focus.

The **Writing Workshop** test provides a passage containing problems or errors in several or all of the following areas: content, organization, style, grammar and usage, and mechanics. Students demonstrate their understanding of the mode of writing and their revising and proofreading skills by revising the essay and correcting the errors. A Revising Guidelines page reminds students of the chapter skills and the basic requirements of the chapter writing mode.

To help students complete the Writing Workshop tests, you may want to give them photocopies of the following page, which lists symbols for revising and proofreading.

Symbols for Revising and Proofreading

The following symbols will help you revise and correct the passages in the
Writing Workshop tests.

SYMBOL	DEFINITION	EXAMPLE
⟿	Delete word.	The girl smiled ~~at me~~.
∧	Insert.	The girl smiled. *at me* ∧
⟋‾	Replace a word.	I found the ~~book~~. *record*
≡	Set in capital letters.	Does karen like fish? ≡
/	Set in lowercase.	Does Karen L̸ike F̸ish?
ⱽ	Insert apostrophe.	Its his dog.
ⱽⱽ	Insert quotation marks.	It's his dog, he said.
⊙	Insert period.	If she goes, I go⊙
⌄	Insert comma.	If she goes I go.
⊙	Insert colon.	Pick a color red, blue, or green.
⌃	Insert semicolon.	We went she stayed.

ELEMENTS OF LANGUAGE | Third Course

Parts of Speech: Overview

A. IDENTIFYING PARTS OF SPEECH On the line provided, identify the part of speech of the italicized word or group of words. Use the following abbreviations:

N	Noun	ADV	Adverb
PRON	Pronoun	PREP	Preposition
ADJ	Adjective	CONJ	Conjunction
V	Verb	INT	Interjection

Example _ADJ_ **1.** *Whose* paintings are on exhibit at the Museum of Modern Art?

_____ **1.** The Museum of Modern Art is located in *New York City*.

_____ **2.** The museum houses *collections* of art from 1880 to the present.

_____ **3.** The exhibits include paintings, sculptures, photographs, *and* much more.

_____ **4.** Built in 1939, the *original* building showcases the International Style of architecture.

_____ **5.** In the 1950s and 1960s, the museum *was expanded*.

_____ **6.** Money to keep the museum open is raised *through* admission fees, contributions, and sales of publications.

_____ **7.** Also located in New York City is the Metropolitan Museum of Art, the *largest* museum of art in the United States.

_____ **8.** It houses over two million works of art, including works from *almost* every culture of the last five thousand years.

_____ **9.** *Wow!* That must be a huge place!

_____ **10.** Although *it* covers four city blocks, the museum cannot display its entire collection at one time.

B. FINDING PARTS OF SPEECH IN SENTENCES In each of the following sentences, underline each word or word group that functions as the part of speech indicated in italics before the sentence.

Example *adverb* **1.** Angelo has been studying quite hard for his science exam today.

noun **11.** One editorial in this newspaper is about freedom of speech.

verb **12.** The dog smelled terrible, so Taryn gave it a bath.

adjective **13.** Surfers and swimmers will soon crowd this California beach.

pronoun **14.** Rita has tried several of the enchilada recipes, but she likes this one best.

preposition **15.** In spite of last week's loss, the team is optimistic about today's game.

adverb	**16.** The Cardonas will arrive in Boulder tomorrow and will stay there until Saturday.
noun	**17.** Barbara Jordan was a member of the House of Representatives for six years.
conjunction	**18.** Taro will play first base, and either Gregory or Jared will play second.
preposition	**19.** Dashing across the outfield, Teresa leaped up and caught the softball with her bare hand.
interjection	**20.** Well, I think these seats will give us a good view of the stage.
verb	**21.** Will you ask him why he did not go on the field trip?
conjunction	**22.** Both Jaime and William were ready to begin rehearsal, but the others had not arrived yet.
pronoun	**23.** Did the toddler injure himself when he fell off the porch?
verb	**24.** If you had asked me sooner, I could have helped with the project.
pronoun	**25.** Is this the book that everyone has been recommending to you?
adverb	**26.** Mrs. Vicente, an exceptionally talented musician, plays the piano and the trumpet equally well.
adjective	**27.** The salad is cool, crisp, and scrumptious.
noun	**28.** The firefighters and the ambulance crew saved many lives that night.
adverb	**29.** Do not stay in the sun too long without sunscreen.
interjection	**30.** Oops! I did not realize that step was so slippery!

C. IDENTIFYING PARTS OF SPEECH On the line provided, identify the part of speech of the italicized word or group of words. Use the following abbreviations:

N	Noun	ADV	Adverb
PRON	Pronoun	PREP	Preposition
ADJ	Adjective	CONJ	Conjunction
V	Verb	INT	Interjection

Example *PREP* **1.** Jalen never goes to the beach *without* his kite.

_____ **31.** At the kite festival, we saw kites of *all* sizes, shapes, and colors.

_____ **32.** A flat kite, the oldest basic type of kite, *needs* a tail to keep it pointed skyward.

_____ **33.** Curved on its face, the bowed kite creates an angle *into* the wind.

_____ **34.** *That* angle, called the dihedral angle, keeps the kite stable without a tail.

_____ **35.** *Have* you ever *seen* a box kite?

_____ **36.** Most of *these* will fly only in strong, steady winds.

_____ **37.** If several box kites are flown on one line, *they* can lift a person off the ground.

_____ **38.** *Yikes!* I wouldn't want to be the person flying those kites!

_____ **39.** Delta kites are triangular *and* have a keel, a flap of material attached to the surface of the kite.

_____ **40.** Easy to build, delta kites fly *readily* in a light wind.

_____ **41.** The parafoil kite, which is *similar* to a parachute, does not have a rigid frame.

_____ **42.** Made entirely of fabric, parafoils take *shape* when they fill with wind.

_____ **43.** I have given some *thought* to buying a stunt kite.

_____ **44.** With *either* two *or* four flying lines, stunt kites can be flown with great precision.

_____ **45.** A skilled operator *can make* a stunt kite perform figure eights, make sharp turns, and even fly backward.

_____ **46.** There was *an* impressive stunt demonstration at the festival.

_____ **47.** The participants maneuvered the kites *extremely* well.

_____ **48.** Kite flying is not just for the windy months of *March* and April.

_____ **49.** In fact, this sport can be *quite* enjoyable almost any time of year.

_____ **50.** However, it would be dangerous to fly a kite *during* a thunderstorm.

The Parts of a Sentence: Subject, Predicate, Complement

A. IDENTIFYING SENTENCES AND REVISING FRAGMENTS Identify each of the following word groups as a sentence or a sentence fragment. On the line provided, write *S* for *sentence* or *F* for *fragment*. Then, revise each fragment to make it a complete sentence.

Example 1. For bicycle rides as a family.

F—They sometimes go for bicycle rides as a family.

1. Everyone in the Levine family enjoys outdoor activities.

_____

2. Mrs. Levine for a hike almost every weekend.

_____

3. Usually takes Mindy and Joshua along.

_____

4. The dog goes, too.

_____

5. Mr. Levine often swimming at a nearby lake.

_____

6. His three nephews often join him.

_____

7. After Mindy attended soccer camp last summer.

_____

8. She also excels in track and field.

_____

9. Becoming a skillful mountain-bike rider.

_____

10. Down the trails on Brown's Mountain.

_____

B. IDENTIFYING COMPLETE SUBJECTS AND SIMPLE SUBJECTS In each of the following sentences, underline the complete subject once and the simple subject twice.

Example 1. At the entrance to the trail is a large warning sign picturing a mountain lion.

11. How long does a young mountain lion stay with its mother?

12. The kittens stay close to their mother for up to two years.

13. An excellent climber, the lynx can easily cross boulders and fallen trees.

14. In winter, the furry feet of the lynx help it move swiftly in deep snow.

15. One very common wildcat in North America is the bobcat.

C. IDENTIFYING COMPLETE PREDICATES AND SIMPLE PREDICATES In each of the following sentences, underline the complete predicate once and the simple predicate twice.

Example 1. Did you see any manatees during your trip to Florida?

16. The Caribbean manatee can be found in the bays and rivers of Florida.

17. In the rivers of western Africa dwells the African manatee.

18. According to an article in this magazine, all three species of manatee are either endangered or threatened.

19. How much does one of these large water mammals weigh?

20. A Caribbean manatee may weigh up to 3,500 pounds.

D. IDENTIFYING SUBJECTS AND VERBS In each of the following sentences, underline the subject once and the verb twice. If *you* is the understood subject, write (*you*) on the line provided. [Hint: A subject or verb may be compound.]

Example _____ **1.** Here are the blueberries and peaches for the fruit salad.

_____ **21.** Blueberry plants live for decades and bear tasty fruit.

_____ **22.** Several of these plants in a row might line the edge of a pond or serve as attractive hedges.

_____ **23.** In the spring, these beautiful plants develop white, bell-shaped flowers.

_____ **24.** Ripening slowly, a single cluster of berries may be green, red, and blue all at one time.

_____ **25.** There are several different species of blueberries.

_____ **26.** Where should blueberries be planted?

_____ **27.** Plant your blueberries in an area with plenty of moisture.

_____ **28.** Full sun and good circulation of air are also important.

_____ **29.** Are blueberries, cranberries, or raisins best with breakfast cereal?

_____ **30.** All of these fruits taste delicious in muffins or with yogurt.

E. IDENTIFYING AND CLASSIFYING COMPLEMENTS Underline all the complements in the following sentences. Classify each complement by writing above it *PN* for *predicate nominative*, *PA* for *predicate adjective*, *DO* for *direct object*, or *IO* for *indirect object*.

Example 1. Aunt Lydia gave Jackie and me a ride to the soccer game.
(IO   IO   DO)

31. At first this Saturday had been a warm, sunny day.

32. However, the sky became grayer and grayer as the fans filed into the stadium.

33. Carefully, Jackie handed me her new binoculars.

34. Grandma had given her the binoculars as an early birthday gift.

35. Through the binoculars I could see our goalkeeper warming up on the sidelines.

36. She and the rest of the team looked strong, healthy, and ready to play.

37. Vanessa, Keesha, and Tina are all forwards; they are mainly responsible for scoring goals.

38. The midfielders, also called halfbacks, unite the offense and defense.

39. Our team did not win the game, but we were proud of their effort.

40. Fortunately, we never did get any rain.

F. CLASSIFYING SENTENCES BY PURPOSE Classify each of the following sentences according to its purpose. On the line provided, write *declarative, imperative, interrogative,* or *exclamatory*.

Example _____*imperative*_____ 1. Look at these strange little lizards.

_____ **41.** Is it true that this pet store does not sell cats or dogs?

_____ **42.** The reptiles were all bred domestically; none were taken from the wild.

_____ **43.** Do you think a rat would make a good pet?

_____ **44.** According to my brother, the hamsters are much cuter.

_____ **45.** Don't handle the ferrets without the help of a clerk.

_____ **46.** In a separate room, you will find the pet birds.

_____ **47.** What a beautiful selection of finches they have!

_____ **48.** Would you prefer a parakeet or a canary?

_____ **49.** Choose one that looks active, healthy, and happy.

_____ **50.** I can't wait to take my new pet home!

The Phrase: Prepositional, Verbal, and Appositive Phrases

A. IDENTIFYING AND CLASSIFYING PREPOSITIONAL PHRASES In each of the following sentences, underline the prepositional phrase. Then, classify each prepositional phrase by writing *ADJ* for *adjective phrase* or *ADV* for *adverb phrase* above the phrase. [Note: A sentence may contain more than one phrase.]

                   ADV   ADJ

Example 1. In spite of her difficult start in life, our dog Cookie is now healthy and happy.

1. We adopted Cookie from the animal shelter a few years ago.

2. At the time, she had a serious ear infection and a case of worms.

3. Cookie had been abandoned early in her life.

4. Fortunately, her stay at the shelter was brief, and she received good medical treatment there.

5. Everyone in our family liked the little mixed-breed pup the first time we saw her.

6. Dad has always been especially fond of her.

7. Although Cookie was somewhat timid during that first meeting, she gradually gained confidence.

8. My brothers and I have given her plenty of care, attention, and love.

9. We have even taught her some tricks; she can now crawl through tunnels and jump hurdles.

10. This little dog definitely has a special place in the heart of each family member.

B. IDENTIFYING VERBALS Each of the following sentences contains a verbal (a participle, a gerund, or an infinitive). Underline each verbal. Then, tell what type of verbal it is by writing *PART* for *participle*, *GER* for *gerund*, or *INF* for *infinitive* above the verbal.

                                                       INF

Example 1. My grandparents have always encouraged me to learn about music, dance, art, and

            theater.

11. According to them, the arts will help me develop into a well-rounded person.

12. When I was younger, I took dance lessons, focusing on tap and ballet.

13. Performing on stage can be scary but also enjoyable.

14. My cousin Zachary is hoping to get the main role in his school play.

15. As a dancer in our school musical, I actually enjoyed rehearsing.

16. I found it easy to learn the samba, a popular Brazilian dance.

17. Anthony, my brother, prefers the visual arts and especially enjoys drawing.

18. Spending hours at his desk, he sometimes creates several artworks in one evening.

19. His dream is to become an illustrator of children's books.

20. Applying techniques from his art class, he made a beautiful pastel landscape.

C. Identifying Verbal Phrases Identify the italicized verbal phrase in each of the following sentences. Above the phrase, write *PART* for *participial phrase,* *GER* for *gerund phrase,* or *INF* for *infinitive phrase.*

Example 1. Harry Belafonte is an American singer *PART* *known for his versions of West Indian songs.*

21. *Sighing deeply,* Emilio opened the test booklet and began.

22. Acupuncture, a way of treating disease by *inserting needles into the body,* started in ancient China.

23. *To paint this wall green* would be a big mistake, in my opinion.

24. Celia Cruz, *known as the Queen of Salsa,* performed traditional Latin music.

25. Lasers can be used *to record music, motion pictures, and computer data on special discs.*

26. *Making origami figures* is one of Mr. Hirami's favorite pastimes.

27. Hakeem, the second runner *to cross the finish line,* seemed pleased with his performance.

28. The pansy is a low-growing, flowering plant *belonging to the violet family.*

29. According to his teacher, David's worst habit is *speaking out of turn.*

30. *Startled by the sudden noise,* the kitten spun around in a circle and darted away.

D. IDENTIFYING APPOSITIVES AND APPOSITIVE PHRASES Underline the appositive or appositive phrase in each of the following sentences.

Example 1. My sister <u>Alexis</u> attends college at the University of New Mexico.

31. Amelia Earhart helped found the Ninety-Nines, an international organization of women pilots.

32. I heard our neighbors' dog, Bandit, barking at about ten o'clock last night.

33. Angela wears her new jacket, a gift from her grandparents, almost every day.

34. Actor Sidney Poitier has appeared both on Broadway and in films.

35. Peking opera, a form of Chinese drama, combines dialogue, music, dancing, and acrobatics.

36. Have you seen Hector's brother, the older one?

37. Someone, maybe the mail carrier, left this note for you, Mom.

38. We made two stops in Florida, Orlando and Tampa, during our trip.

39. A national treasure, the original copy of the Declaration of Indpendence is displayed in the National Archives Building in Washington, D.C.

40. They are looking for volunteers, any people who can bring a pickup truck, to help on Saturday.

ELEMENTS OF LANGUAGE | Third Course

E. IDENTIFYING PHRASES For each of the following sentences, identify the italicized phrase by writing *PREP* for *prepositional*, *PART* for *participial*, *GER* for *gerund*, *INF* for *infinitive*, or *APP* for *appositive* above the phrase.

                                                 GER

Example 1. Everyone enjoyed *seeing Uncle Marco's slides of Lisbon, Portugal*.

41. Around A.D. 1200, Lisbon was chosen *to be the capital of Portugal*.

42. *Overlooking the mouth of the Tagus River*, Lisbon is a major port and cultural center.

43. Lisbon's downtown district is a low, flat area *next to the harbor*.

44. This area, *called the Baixa*, is home to most of Lisbon's fine shops.

45. Lisbon has many public squares and statues dedicated *to national heroes*.

46. One of these heroes is Vasco da Gama, *a world-famous explorer*.

47. The Tower of Belem was built in the early 1500s *to honor him*.

48. Many tourists are interested in *visiting the castle of Sao Jorge and the Sao Carlos Opera House*.

49. The 25th of April Bridge, *one of the world's longest suspension bridges*, spans the Tagus River.

50. *Shipping, especially of Portuguese products such as ceramics, cork, and sardines*, is vital to Lisbon's economy.

The Clause: Independent and Subordinate Clauses

A. IDENTIFYING INDEPENDENT AND SUBORDINATE CLAUSES   For each of the following sentences, identify the clause in italics as independent or subordinate. Above the clause, write *IND* for *independent* or *SUB* for *subordinate*.

Example 1. Many athletes remember Alice Coachman *because she helped break down barriers for both women and African Americans.*   SUB

1. *When she was a child,* Alice Coachman would challenge others in her neighborhood to running and jumping contests.

2. *She began formal sports training in fifth grade,* after a teacher recognized her great talent.

3. While at Tuskegee Institute High School in the 1940s, *Coachman captured national track and field championships in four different events.*

4. *As World War II came to an end,* she looked forward to entering international competitions.

5. The 1948 Olympics were held in London, England, and *Alice Coachman was there.*

6. She won the gold medal in the running high jump, a feat *that earned her special recognition in the sports world as the first African American woman to win an Olympic gold medal.*

7. After the Olympics, Coachman left athletics; *she became a physical education teacher and also earned a bachelor's degree in home economics.*

8. Alice Coachman did not experience the kind of publicity *that today's athletes enjoy,* but she was nevertheless recognized as a hero in both the United States and England.

9. She was honored in 1975 *when she was inducted into the National Track and Field Hall of Fame.*

10. At the age of sixty, she said, "*As I look back,* I wonder why I worked so hard, put so much time into it—but I guess it's just I wanted to win."

B. IDENTIFYING AND CLASSIFYING SUBORDINATE CLAUSES   Underline the subordinate clause in each of the following sentences. Then, above the clause, classify each subordinate clause by writing *ADJ* for *adjective clause, ADV* for *adverb clause,* or *N* for *noun clause.*

Example 1. <u>When I visited the Steinhart Aquarium in San Francisco</u>, I started to think about   ADV
having a little aquarium of my own.

11. I did not know what would be required, so I did some research.

12. After I had read a book about the basics of aquarium maintenance, I discussed the idea with my parents.

13. Where I would get help with this project was my stepmother's main concern.

14. I remembered that my aunt Nari has always had aquariums, so I called her.

15. Aunt Nari is happy to help anyone who shows an interest in her favorite hobby.

16. She helped me choose the equipment that would be right for me.

17. We made a list of supplies so that we would remember to get everything at the pet store.

18. I decided to use plastic plants, which make tank maintenance easier.

19. We filled the tank a little at a time and put the filter in just before the tank was full.

20. After the tank was filled, we waited several days before getting the fish.

21. Did you know that it takes two to three days for the water to be livable for fish?

22. Aunt Nari told me to choose fish that do not tend to fight or chase other fish.

23. Since I am a beginner, it was also a good idea to get hardy, inexpensive types of fish.

24. I started with a few angelfish and neon tetras, which are popular fish for beginners.

25. When the first fish were used to the tank, I gradually added more.

26. What I have learned most of all from setting up my aquarium is patience.

27. Needless to say, I am pleased about how well my aquarium project has gone.

28. At the first sign of a problem with my aquarium, I call Mr. Lynch, who owns a pet store.

29. He is very knowledgeable and always helps me when I need advice.

30. I am always eager to show my aquarium to whoever wants to see it.

C. CLASSIFYING SUBORDINATE CLAUSES Classify the italicized subordinate clause in each of the following sentences. Above the clause, write *ADJ* for *adjective clause,* *ADV* for *adverb clause,* or *N* for *noun clause.* For each adjective or adverb clause, also write the word or words that the clause modifies. For each noun clause, tell how the noun clause is used by writing *S* for *subject,* *PN* for *predicate nominative,* *DO* for *direct object,* or *OP* for *object of a preposition.*

Examples 1. Anyone *who wants salad* should order it separately. *ADJ—Anyone*

2. Bonus points will be awarded to *whoever turns in the assignment early.* *N—OP*

31. The puppy *that is sitting in the corner* seems very shy.

32. Mr. Franklin believes *that Mahalia Jackson was the best gospel singer ever.*

33. *What Dr. Chan said* has started to worry me.

34. Tennis player Bjorn Borg, *who had a calm manner on the court,* was nicknamed "The Iceman."

35. *Because there are so many different kinds of burritos*, we enjoy having them for supper at least once a week.

36. Judy Garland first appeared on stage *when she was only five years old*.

37. Do you know if the media center has any CD-ROMs about *how volcanoes are formed*?

38. *Unless the weather improves*, the trail ride will be canceled.

39. Tomorrow in music class, Tamala will give her presentation, *which is about Maria Callas, the famous opera singer*.

40. Commercial art is *what Russell will study in college*.

D. CLASSIFYING SENTENCES ACCORDING TO STRUCTURE On the line provided, classify each sentence according to structure. Write *S* for *simple sentence, CD* for *compound sentence, CX* for *complex sentence,* or *CD-CX* for *compound-complex sentence.*

Example _CD-CX_ **1.** Mr. Turner is an anthropologist, and last year he traveled to Canada, where he lived with a Cree Indian family for several months.

_____ **41.** Although most Cree live in Canada, about two thousand live in the United States on a reservation in Montana.

_____ **42.** The Cree, who form a number of bands, speak dialects of an Algonquian language.

_____ **43.** The woodlands of eastern and northern Canada were once home to all of the Cree.

_____ **44.** They began to trade with Europeans in the late 1600s, and in the mid-1700s some Cree bands moved onto the plains.

_____ **45.** Those who moved west were called the Plains Cree, and they became buffalo hunters.

_____ **46.** The Cree who remained in the forest continued in the fur trade.

_____ **47.** They became known as the Woodlands Cree.

_____ **48.** The Woodlands Cree used to live in tents that were covered with hides or birchbark, but now most of them live in cabins or frame houses.

_____ **49.** Today many Cree farm on reservations; others live in cities in Canada.

_____ **50.** Some Cree are employed by the Canadian government as healthcare workers, teachers, and clerks.

Agreement: Subject and Verb; Pronoun and Antecedent

A. IDENTIFYING VERBS THAT AGREE IN NUMBER WITH THEIR SUBJECTS In each of the following sentences, underline the correct form of the verb in parentheses.

Example 1. Neither the coach nor the players (*was*, <u>*were*</u>) pleased with the referee's call.

1. Backstage, a few of the dancers (*is*, *are*) preparing for the next scene.

2. Both Maria and Brooke (*admires*, *admire*) Pablo Casals, the famous cellist.

3. (*Doesn't*, *Don't*) this photograph show all the cast members in the play?

4. After practice Annette or James usually (*helps*, *help*) with the equipment.

5. Many a sailor (*has*, *have*) learned to respect the brutal storms in these seas.

6. Where (*is*, *are*) the instructions for this printer?

7. The penguin's body surface has short, thick feathers that (*provides*, *provide*) waterproofing.

8. (*Is*, *Are*) *The Outsiders* on the reading list?

9. The siding on both of those houses (*needs*, *need*) to be painted.

10. Most of the cookbook (*is*, *are*) dedicated to traditional Japanese dishes.

11. The dinners we made last night (*was*, *were*) delivered to people in need.

12. Within minutes, two thirds of the burrito (*was*, *were*) gone.

13. Everyone on the soccer team (*wears*, *wear*) shinguards.

14. The hula dancers (*was*, *were*) the first act in the talent show.

15. On Saturdays either Michael or his parents (*walks*, *walk*) to the city market to buy fresh fruit.

16. The audience (*was*, *were*) silent during Toni Morrison's lecture.

17. This year civics (*seems*, *seem*) to be Clarissa's favorite subject.

18. (*Has*, *Have*) any of the buses been on time today?

19. Our gym teacher and basketball coach (*is*, *are*) Mr. Johnson.

20. We enjoyed the blues concert, but two hours (*was*, *were*) too long to wait in line.

B. IDENTIFYING ANTECEDENTS AND WRITING PRONOUNS Each of the following sentences contains a line where a personal pronoun should be. On each line, write an appropriate personal pronoun, making sure that it agrees with its antecedent. Underline the antecedent.

Example 1. Did <u>Adam</u> or <u>Jonathan</u> leave _____*his*_____ uniform on the bus?

21. During the swimming lesson, several of the children asked _____ parents for help.

22. Actress Rita Moreno won an Academy Award for _____ role in *West Side Story*.

23. Either Randall or Jim will do _____ presentation on Jacob Lawrence, whose paintings

portray the daily lives of African Americans in the mid-twentieth century.

24. Grand Rapids has a population approaching 220,000, making _____ the second-largest

city in Michigan.

25. I offered her ten dollars for the ticket, but she said _____ wasn't enough.

26. Will each of the girls bring _____ own volleyball?

27. Ricardo is a dedicated worker who always does _____ best.

28. Nearly all of the leaves have fallen; you might as well begin raking _____ into piles.

29. At the end of baseball season, the team emptied _____ lockers.

30. Latrice and Bernie subscribe to that travel magazine because _____ enjoy reading about

faraway lands.

C. PROOFREADING SENTENCES FOR SUBJECT-VERB AND PRONOUN-ANTECEDENT AGREEMENT Most
of the following sentences contain errors in agreement. Draw a line through each incorrect verb or
pronoun, and write the correct form above it. If a sentence is already correct, write *C* on the line
provided.

Example _____ **1.** The two tickets to the band competition in Toronto ~~doesn't~~ *don't* cost much.

_____ **31.** Many a driver on the roads these days wish that others would not use cell phones

while driving.

_____ **32.** Mrs. Caldwell explained that *God's Trombones* are a book of poems by James Weldon

Johnson.

_____ **33.** After a short break, Hannah and Ramon will give their yoga demonstration.

_____ **34.** Don't this chicken curry look delicious?

_____ **35.** My cousin Reynard is studying physics and finding them less difficult than he

had expected.

_____ **36.** Neither of the kittens sleep during the night.

_____ **37.** As the curtain rose, both of the dancers took their places on stage.

_____ **38.** Someone on the girls' basketball team has left their shoes in the gym.

_____ **39.** One weekend a month, the whole family pile into the van to go visit Grandmother and

Grandfather.

_____ **40.** There's several different daily newspapers published in New York City.

_____ **41.** Each Wednesday evening, either Velma or her brother take out the trash.

_____ **42.** Do you think six dollars are too much for admission to the museum?

_____ **43.** Most of the dishes at that Vietnamese restaurant contains rice or noodles.

_____ **44.** Either Shanda or Gloria decided to do their report on Fats Waller, the famous jazz

pianist.

_____ **45.** A dog that is loyal and obedient to their master is always cherished.

_____ **46.** Has the food and the first-aid kit been packed yet?

_____ **47.** Obviously, the people at the Corn Dance Fiesta is enjoying the celebration.

_____ **48.** Some of the paper is a little damp, but it will dry quickly.

_____ **49.** Actually, my favorite act at the circus were the jugglers.

_____ **50.** Few that will be running in the marathon has finished a race this long before.

Using Verbs Correctly: Principal Parts, Tense, Voice, Mood

A. PROOFREADING SENTENCES FOR CORRECT VERB FORMS   Most of the following sentences contain errors in the use of verbs. Draw a line through each incorrect verb form, and write the correct form above it. If a sentence is already correct, write *C* on the line provided.

Example _____ **1.** How many laps have you ~~swam~~ *swum* so far?

_____ **1.** Elena has grew two inches in just one year.

_____ **2.** On September 1, 1923, a terrible earthquake shaked Tokyo, Japan, and destroyed much of the city.

_____ **3.** Eric tossed his cleats on the chair and turns on the stereo.

_____ **4.** The Inca wrote dramas that described military victories.

_____ **5.** Mr. and Mrs. Sierro drived all day to get to Seattle.

_____ **6.** The field of commercial art has expanded greatly over the years.

_____ **7.** According to this article, Federico Fabian Peña has served as mayor of Denver, Colorado, from 1983 until 1991.

_____ **8.** For many years, Mr. Montero has teached flamenco dancing.

_____ **9.** Has Theo rode his new bicycle yet?

_____ **10.** The dog sprinted across the field, jumped up, and catches the ball in his teeth.

_____ **11.** The governor has visited some of the tornado victims, and tomorrow he holds a brief press conference.

_____ **12.** Have you always knew so much about traditional African rituals?

_____ **13.** Yesterday, Kisha brung *Tortuga*, a novel by Rudolfo Anaya, home from the library.

_____ **14.** How much of the chicken fried rice have the guests eaten?

_____ **15.** Karl heard an eerie noise, and immediately he freezes with fear.

_____ **16.** At the end of last week, the International Club goes to the National Museum of African Art in Washington, D.C.

_____ **17.** I wish I still had those notes, but I throwed them out months ago.

_____ **18.** Markita watches carefully as Mr. Grayson assembled the swing set.

_____ **19.** Has Toby ever flew in a small plane before?

_____ **20.** At the University of California, softball pitcher Michele Granger breaked the NCAA record for strikeouts.

B. CHANGING TENSES OF VERBS In each of the following sentences, change the tense of the verb to the tense indicated in brackets. Underline the original verb form, and write the new form above it.

Example 1. Mr. Batista <u>searched</u> for the lost puppy for hours. [*past perfect, progressive form*]
had been searching (written above "searched")

21. The Wong family lived in San Francisco for fifteen years. [*present perfect*]

22. Julia took conga lessons for three years. [*past perfect, progressive form*]

23. On Saturday morning, Derek will make tortilla soup, a popular Mexican dish, for the family's lunch. [*past*]

24. Mr. Jee helped us with our chemistry project. [*present perfect, progressive form*]

25. At the festival a group of Hopi performed portions of their snake dance ceremony. [*future*]

26. Marcelo read *Up from Slavery* all afternoon. [*future, progressive form*]

27. Margaret will paint the bathroom walls pale yellow. [*present, progressive form*]

28. By that time Brandon had finished most of his household chores. [*future perfect*]

29. In the summer my sister and I will mow lawns in our neighborhood. [*present*]

30. Chuck rinsed each glass thoroughly in clean, warm water. [*past perfect*]

C. IDENTIFYING ACTIVE AND PASSIVE VOICE Tell whether each of the following sentences is in the active or the passive voice. On the line provided, write *AV* for *active voice* or *PV* for *passive voice*.

Example _AV_ **1.** Some of your ancestors may have entered the United States through Ellis Island.

_____ **31.** For more than sixty years, Ellis Island served as a reception center for immigrants to the United States.

_____ **32.** During the late 1700s, the island was owned by Samuel Ellis, a merchant and farmer.

_____ **33.** In 1808, the U.S. government bought the island.

_____ **34.** The island's peak years as an immigration station lasted from 1892 to 1924.

_____ **35.** At this station, immigrants were checked by doctors and interviewed by government officials.

_____ **36.** The government did not allow people with infectious diseases or criminals into the country.

_____ **37.** Ellis Island, now a national historic site, is managed by the National Park Service.

_____ **38.** The Ellis Island Immigration Museum displays exhibits of old clothing, toys, and passports that belonged to immigrants.

_____ **39.** The American Immigrant Wall of Honor was created in 1990.

_____ **40.** The wall, which stands outside the museum, contains the names of nearly 200,000

immigrants.

D. IDENTIFYING THE CORRECT FORMS OF *LIE* **AND** *LAY, SIT* **AND** *SET,* **AND** *RISE* **AND** *RAISE* Underline
the correct verb in parentheses in each of the following sentences.

Example 1. The deckhands (*rose, raised*) the sail to catch the wind.

41. Finally, Jackie (*sat, set*) a bowl of Chinese rice porridge on the table in front of me.

42. Some peaks in the central ranges of the Pyrenees Mountains (*rise, raise*) over 10,000 feet.

43. Has Vivian already (*lain, laid*) the warm tortillas in the basket?

44. Dad is concerned because the baby's temperature has been (*rising, raising*) all day.

45. The directions to the National Civil Rights Museum are (*lying, laying*) on top of the TV.

46. Please (*lie, lay*) down and rest; I will call the doctor.

47. The Kwanzaa celebration has (*risen, raised*) the spirits of all our family members.

48. How long have you been (*sitting, setting*) here on the porch?

49. Most of the dogs (*lay, laid*) quietly as they waited for their turn in the obedience competition.

50. I hope Dana will (*sit, set*) next to me at the concert.

Using Pronouns Correctly: Nominative and Objective Uses; Clear Reference

A. Choosing Correct Pronoun Forms   Underline the correct pronoun form in parentheses in each of the following sentences.

Example   **1.** Marcus has visited more aquariums than (<u>I</u>, me).

1. Last week Uncle Cliff took Tamika and (I, me) to the National Aquarium in Baltimore.

2. As expected, (we, us) girls had a terrific time there and also learned a great deal about all kinds of marine life.

3. Uncle Cliff, (who, whom) is a marine biologist, had plenty to say about the various animals.

4. Between you and (I, me), I had never realized just how knowledgeable my uncle was.

5. The aquarium guide and (he, him) had a long discussion about hammerhead sharks.

6. The most talkative people in our group were some students and (they, them).

7. No one was more interested in their discussions than Tamika and (I, me).

8. During feeding time, the sharks gave a little boy and (we, us) a scare.

9. The turtles and (they, them) were the most spectacular creatures there.

10. Tamika and I will always remember (they, them).

B. Choosing Correct Pronoun Forms and Identifying Case   Underline the correct pronoun form in parentheses in each of the following sentences. Then, identify the case of the pronoun by writing *NOM* for *nominative* or *OBJ* for *objective* above the underlined pronoun.

Example   **1.** Are Mr. Campos and (<u>she</u>, her) helping with the blood drive this year? [NOM]

11. The two faculty advisors for the play are (he and she, him and her), I believe.

12. Has the conflict between Rodney and (he, him) finally been resolved?

13. Aunt Michi gave the boys and (I, me) tickets to a Midori concert.

14. The only person to try the fish tacos was (she, her).

15. Have Tranh and (they, them) heard this song by Sarah Vaughan, the famous jazz singer?

16. Ms. Santana recognized my brother and (we, us) immediately.

17. My dad will bring some juice and crackers for you and (she, her).

18. At tomorrow's game, either Felicia or (I, me) will play center.

19. A museum guide showed Bryant and (they, them) the display of Ugandan sculptures.

20. Mr. Fallon will help Ray with his costume, and Mom will help Justine and (I, me).

C. PROOFREADING SENTENCES FOR CORRECT PRONOUN FORMS Most of the following sentences contain pronouns that have been used incorrectly. Draw a line through each incorrect pronoun, and write the correct form above the incorrect pronoun. If a sentence is already correct, write *C* on the line provided.

Example _____ **1.** Today's speakers, Colonel Peck and ~~her,~~ *she* will need the overhead projector

and a chalkboard.

_____ **21.** Have you been taking piano lessons as long as her?

_____ **22.** Do his sister and him have Cuban ancestors?

_____ **23.** Mrs. Dixon, who I work for, owns two auto repair shops.

_____ **24.** The actors Timothy most admires are Hector Elizondo and he.

_____ **25.** If you wait for Jamal and I, we will give you a ride.

_____ **26.** Mom took our cousin and we to the Gates Planetarium in Denver.

_____ **27.** Finally, the team—Tammy, Cecilia, and him—began to coordinate their efforts.

_____ **28.** Has anyone heard whom the new class president will be?

_____ **29.** Did Mr. Osaka leave Rusty and she at the pool?

_____ **30.** Karli made Dad and he some delicious Vietnamese spring rolls for dinner.

_____ **31.** After practice Coach Jackson spoke individually with the two point guards, Cody

and me.

_____ **32.** Nobody enjoys the music of Shakira more than me.

_____ **33.** Everyone except Eli and she will be going on the field trip to the Indian Pueblo

Cultural Center.

_____ **34.** Today in American history class, Ellen and them will give their report on the life of

Frederick Douglass.

_____ **35.** The first performer to arrive at rehearsal was me.

_____ **36.** Has Teresa already sent Grandma and they a thank-you note?

_____ **37.** Ms. Agoyo, whom guided her class in exploring Web sites on Civil War battlefields,

has assigned group reports.

_____ **38.** When you serve the salad, give yourself less than he.

_____ **39.** Is Langston Hughes the poet to whom you are referring?

_____ **40.** Please give we band members your support.

D. CORRECTING UNCLEAR PRONOUN REFERENCE On the line provided, revise each of the following sentences, correcting each unclear pronoun reference.

> **Example 1.** We are going to learn engraving in art class, which should be challenging but fun.
>
> *Learning engraving in art class should be challenging but fun.*

41. At that museum they have an exhibit of sculptures by Marisol.

_____

42. The winds were high and the sea was choppy; this made the ship's journey dangerous.

_____

43. Mr. Freeman praised my musical abilities and urged me to consider it as a career.

_____

44. In this article it explains how penguins care for their young.

_____

45. Mom spoke to Lisa about the camping trip as soon as she got home.

_____

46. The kitten is not feeling well; that is obvious.

_____

47. Brian told me that Michael broke his fishing rod.

_____

48. Whenever Evan sees a dance performance, he thinks about becoming one.

_____

49. Kristen stayed up too late, which explains why she looks so tired.

_____

50. In Chapter 3, it describes the art of Romare Bearden.

_____

Using Modifiers Correctly: Comparison and Placement

A. USING ADJECTIVES AND ADVERBS CORRECTLY IN SENTENCES Underline the correct form of the modifier in parentheses in each of the following sentences.

Example 1. We are (*real, really*) optimistic and excited about our string quartet.

1. Jenny, Yori, Cora, and I were all doing (*good, well*) in the school orchestra.

2. We could play our instruments fairly (*skillful, skillfully*) but wanted to play even better.

3. To help motivate ourselves, we practiced (*regular, regularly*) three or four times a week.

4. Since our group included two violinists, a violist, and a cellist, the quartet began to take shape (*quick, quickly*).

5. I admit that as a quartet we sounded rather (*bad, badly*) at first.

6. Our progress seemed so terribly (*slow, slowly*) that we thought we would never play well enough to perform before an audience.

7. As the days went on, though, all of us could hear that we were making (*gradual, gradually*) improvement.

8. We (*slow, slowly*) began to imagine one day playing at a wedding or banquet.

9. We feel that our playing now is almost (*good, well*) enough for us to try our first public appearance.

10. However, we are going to practice more first to make as sure as we can that it doesn't go (*bad, badly*).

B. USING COMPARATIVE AND SUPERLATIVE FORMS CORRECTLY On the line in each of the following sentences, write the correct comparative or superlative form of the modifier that is given in italics before the sentence.

Example *healthy* **1.** Both kittens are adorable, but the white one looks ____healthier____.

difficult **11.** Which is _____ to make, the chow mein or the fried rice?

frequently **12.** Aunt Yolanda visits us _____ than Aunt Colleen does.

great **13.** According to Mr. Cruz, Diego Rivera is the _____ muralist who ever lived.

far **14.** Which of these five ropes will reach _____?

bad **15.** Not trying at all is _____ than trying but failing.

well **16.** Karen speaks Spanish _____ now than she did last year.

ELEMENTS OF LANGUAGE | Third Course

pretty **17.** Aren't these the _____ flowers you have ever seen?

many **18.** Of all the players, Mark made the _____ free throws.

rich **19.** I think this kind of potting soil is _____ than that kind.

famous **20.** Isn't *Native Son* the _____ of all Richard Wright's books?

C. PROOFREADING SENTENCES FOR THE CORRECT USE OF MODIFIERS

Each of the following sentences contains an error in the use of modifiers. To correct each sentence, draw a line through the error and, where necessary, write the correction in the space above. If a sentence requires the addition of a word or words, use a caret ($_\wedge$) to show where the addition should be inserted.

Examples 1. That is the ~~most~~ cutest guinea pig I have ever seen.

                                 the head of

     2. The head of a wolf is wider than $_\wedge$ a German shepherd dog.

21. The annual precipitation in Alaska is greater than Minnesota.

22. I prefer apples because they taste less sweeter than peaches.

23. According to the tour book, the climate of Paris, France, is cooler and drier than Rome, Italy.

24. Tokyo's commuter trains are some of the most efficientest in the world.

25. In yesterday's game, Brandi had more base hits than anyone on her team.

26. Which is least difficult to train, a Dalmatian or a bulldog?

27. Is the Vikings' winning streak really two games longer than the Cougars?

28. Little Ashley grew more quieter as she listened to the bedtime story.

29. Nancy Lopez became one of the more successful players in the history of women's golf.

30. Cordell probably knows more about Zora Neale Hurston's work than any student in his class.

31. The winds of a tornado are even stronger than a hurricane.

32. In the 1400s, the Aztecs had one of the more advanced cultures in the Americas.

33. New York City has a larger population than any city in the United States.

34. Jeffrey studies with Pablo less than Adam.

35. Mount Fuji is the highest and bestest-known mountain peak in Japan.

36. California has more American Indians than any state except Oklahoma.

37. Of the two books, *The Woman Warrior* is shortest.

38. That science test was much more easier than I thought it would be.

39. Which of those four vehicles is more reliable?

40. Van has logged more volunteer hours than anyone in his family.

Chapter Tests

D. CORRECTING DANGLING AND MISPLACED MODIFIERS Most of the following sentences contain dangling or misplaced modifiers. On the line provided, revise each incorrect sentence so that the meaning is clear. If a sentence is already correct, write C on the line.

Example 1. Sitting on the beach, the soft breeze felt cool and refreshing.

The soft breeze felt cool and refreshing to me as I sat on the beach.

41. Eager to go, the car was quickly packed, and we headed for the beach.

_____

42. Napping in the car, my younger sister dreamed of starfish and baby turtles.

_____

43. To get to the cottage, a narrow, bumpy road was the only way through the dunes.

_____

44. I watched sailboats skim over the waves with my binoculars.

_____

45. Our dog Buster chased a sea gull barking gleefully.

_____

46. Using paper cups and old spoons, a sand castle was built.

_____

47. Darryl and I looked for seashells covered with sunscreen.

_____

48. Exhausted after our swim, the dry towels and soft sand looked inviting.

_____

49. Melissa and I rode bicycles the next day that we had rented.

_____

50. We found a little shop where we bought souvenirs of our visit.

_____

CHAPTER TEST

A Glossary of Usage: Common Usage Problems

A. SOLVING COMMON USAGE PROBLEMS In each of the following sentences, underline the word or expression in parentheses that is correct according to standard, formal usage.

Example 1. Did Texas have (*fewer, less*) tornadoes this year (*than, then*) last year?

1. (*Can, May*) I (*borrow, loan*) your copy of *Crusade for Justice*?

2. It is (*a, an*) honor to be nominated for student council.

3. He didn't realize he was putting too much helium in the balloon until it (*burst, busted*).

4. You (*had ought to, should*) do (*your, you're*) report on the Mochica people of Peru.

5. (*Them, Those*) posters are more expensive (*than, then*) the one I bought.

6. One reason that my stepsister Nikki does (*good, well*) in school is (*that, because*) she has good study habits.

7. Nari trimmed the bonsai tree just (*like, as*) Mr. Botan had (*learned, taught*) her.

8. What treats did Mother put (*inside of, inside*) the piñata?

9. In 1990, Octavio Paz (*accepted, excepted*) the Nobel Prize in literature.

10. Malcolm, would you please (*bring, take*) (*this here, this*) life jacket with you when you leave for the lake later?

11. Although the patient's condition has improved (*somewhat, some*), some of the doctors are still concerned.

12. I am (*rather, kind of*) reluctant to drive such a long (*ways, way*) just to go shopping.

13. The baskets, woven by Pomo artisans, are decorated with shells, feathers, (*etc., and etc.*)

14. Didn't (*nobody, anybody*) know that Granville T. Woods (*discovered, invented*) the railway telegraph system in 1887?

15. Every teacher (*accept, except*) Mr. Lang assigned (*a lot, alot*) of homework today.

16. Mr. Torres looked for white corn tortillas, but the market didn't have (*any, none*).

17. In sailing, "trimming" (*is when you adjust, means adjusting*) the sails to take the best advantage of the wind.

18. Although Martha likes Japanese food, she usually (*don't, doesn't*) get (*no, any*) sushi.

19. I must (*have, of*) left my glasses in the other room.

20. Our dog Rudy (*used to, use to*) be very athletic, but these days he (*can't, can*) hardly even climb the stairs.

B. CORRECTING USAGE ERRORS Most of the following sentences contain errors in usage. Draw a line through each error and, where necessary, write the correct word or words above the error. If a sentence is already correct, write *C* on the line provided.

Example _____ **1.** Last Saturday I went to a dog show with my aunt Sylvia, ~~which~~ *who* breeds Boston terriers.

_____ **21.** There must of been five hundred dogs in that arena!

_____ **22.** I hadn't never seen that many dogs in one place before.

_____ **23.** Although the group competitions were suppose to begin at 1:00, they actually did not start until about 1:30.

_____ **24.** However, the waiting didn't hardly affect my good mood.

_____ **25.** The judges they choose the dog that best conforms to the standard for its breed.

_____ **26.** It was a beautiful collie what won the herding group.

_____ **27.** My aunt's dog won its breed, but that was all the farther it got in the competition.

_____ **28.** There weren't no hard feelings among the people whose dogs did not win.

_____ **29.** I read where terriers were originally bred to pursue prey by digging into the ground.

_____ **30.** These type of dogs hunted rodents, badgers, rabbits, and other small animals.

_____ **31.** Beside the conformation competition, the dog show also included obedience trials and a canine freestyle demonstration.

_____ **32.** In canine freestyle, the owner and dog perform a routine to music, almost like they are dance partners.

_____ **33.** How did that owner learn her dog to do those complicated moves?

_____ **34.** Activities such as canine freestyle help strengthen the bond between a person and his or her dog.

_____ **35.** The second person in the obedience competition seemed very confident of hisself and of his dog.

_____ **36.** Moving with grace and precision, they performed their routine especially good.

_____ **37.** Try to imagine how much training is required to win an obedience competition.

_____ **38.** At first a dog don't know what any commands mean.

_____ **39.** You can't train no dog well unless you are patient and consistent.

_____ **40.** The focus and discipline of them dogs in the obedience ring amazed me.

C. USING NONSEXIST LANGUAGE   In each of the following sentences, draw a line through any gender-specific terms. Then, write a nonsexist term above the term you have crossed out.

Example   1. The book was about the relationship between ~~mankind~~ *human beings* and the natural world.

41. To finish the park cleanup on time, we will need more manpower.

42. This book of consumer advice is popular with housewives.

43. Management does not always choose the best man for the job.

44. Please write to your senator immediately to urge him to support the bill.

45. Are there any salesmen working in this department?

46. Does your dog always bark at deliverymen?

47. Everyone in our school has his own locker.

48. As the blaze raged on, the firemen made several daring rescues.

49. Some man-made fibers, such as rayon, are made from wood pulp.

50. What are the city's requirements for becoming a policeman?

Capital Letters: The Rules for Capitalization

A. CORRECTING ERRORS IN CAPITALIZATION Most of the following items contain errors in capitalization. Correct each error by rewriting the item, correctly capitalized, on the line provided. If an item is already correct, write *C* on the line.

Example 1. the eiffel tower _____*the Eiffel Tower*_____

1. a mexican american _____

2. the roman goddess minerva _____

3. a gift from uncle Horace _____

4. a ride on the *orient express* _____

5. a Chevrolet truck _____

6. the Lincoln Memorial _____

7. the andes mountains in south america _____

8. driving west on Mulberry Avenue _____

9. the play *A Raisin in the sun* _____

10. the houston comets _____

11. professor Lisa Kwan _____

12. the girl scouts of the u.s.a. _____

13. Chemistry II, algebra, and Spanish _____

14. nova scotia, a province in Canada _____

15. *the wizard of oz* _____

16. a passage from the Bible _____

17. the mekong river in vietnam _____

18. an academy award _____

19. harding's bakery on alameda avenue _____

20. studying the Hoover Dam in history class _____

B. USING CAPITAL LETTERS CORRECTLY In the following sentences, underline each word that should begin with a capital letter.

Example 1. Our week in <u>denver</u>, <u>colorado</u>, was so exciting <u>i</u> didn't want to leave.

21. during our vacation there, my mother, my grandmother, and i stayed with some friends on

    maplewood avenue.

22. on monday we visited the home of molly brown, a famous survivor of the sinking of the *titanic.*

23. the next day mom and i toured the denver zoo while grandma shopped at larimer square.

24. at the zoo everyone chuckled when a little boy yelled, "hey, do they have any dinosaurs in this place?"

25. we all enjoyed the show about saturn at the gates planetarium.

26. union station, a historic landmark, has amtrak train service.

27. our friend and hostess, mrs. coleman, told us that the moffat tunnel was completed in 1927.

28. according to the colemans, after the denver pacific railroad was completed in 1870, the city began to grow.

29. we learned more about the city's history at the colorado history museum.

30. for me, the highlight of the week was watching the broncos play the dolphins at mile high stadium.

C. CORRECTING ERRORS IN CAPITALIZATION Each of the following sentences contains at least one error in capitalization. Correct each error by crossing out the incorrect letter and writing the correct form above it.

Example 1. In Egyptian mythology, the ~~M~~oon ~~G~~od was called ~~k~~honsu.
                                         m   *g*   *K*

31. In march the Feldmans will observe passover, which celebrates the israelites' freedom from slavery in Egypt.

32. The last line of my Poem is "protect the animals, o mighty one."

33. In science class we saw a Documentary on the space shuttle *columbia*.

34. Mr. gardner told us that dr. charles drew received the spingarn medal in 1944.

35. The koran contains the sacred writings of Islam.

36. The spacecraft *galileo* began orbiting jupiter in December 1995.

37. Marion began her letter "dear granddad," and signed it "warmly, Marion."

38. Medical research associates, inc., recently moved to 121 elm lane in columbus.

39. Clarissa asked, "aren't mercury, venus, earth, and mars the four Planets that are closest to the Sun?"

40. Henry b. gonzalez was elected to the House of representatives in 1961.

D. CORRECTING ERRORS IN CAPITALIZATION Each of the following sentences contains at least one error in capitalization. Correct each error by crossing out the incorrect letter and writing the correct form above it.

Example 1. ~~i~~n ~~A~~rt class, we studied the collages of ~~r~~omare ~~b~~earden.

41. romare bearden was born in charlotte, north carolina, and grew up in pittsburgh and new york city.

42. At the art students league in new york city, bearden studied with the german artist george grosz.

43. Bearden was also influenced by e. sims campbell, a cartoonist.

44. In fact, for a time, bearden was Cartoonist for the *baltimore afro-american.*

45. As an artist bearden was influenced by the italian Renaissance and by the dutch painters of the 1600s, among others.

46. He is best known for his colorful, large-scale collages, which explore various aspects of african american culture.

47. Many of Bearden's works, such as his oil Painting *at the savoy,* show the influence of Jazz and Blues music on his Style.

48. In 1971, the museum of modern art featured Bearden's work in a major retrospective show.

49. He was awarded the national medal of the arts in 1987.

50. To learn more about this brilliant Artist, read the book *Romare Bearden: his life and art.*

Punctuation: End Marks, Abbreviations, and Commas

A. CORRECTING SENTENCES BY ADDING END MARKS Insert end marks (periods, exclamation points, and question marks) where they are needed in the following sentences.

EXAMPLE 1. Mr. Sato asked if I would like to learn about the art of bonsai.

1. Bonsai, the art of growing miniature trees, originated in China and Japan

2. Have you ever seen any of these tiny trees

3. How amazing this bonsai forest is

4. Bonsai artists strive to create small trees that look just like large trees in nature

5. Grow your bonsai tree in a tray or other container

6. Will you start with an ordinary young tree, a seedling, or a cutting

7. Pinch off new growth, and put wire on the branches to control the tree's size and shape

8. Pruning the roots and branches keeps the trees small

9. Add rocks and mosses to make your bonsai forest even more beautiful

10. What an engaging hobby this is

B. USING ABBREVIATIONS CORRECTLY On the line provided, rewrite each of the following sentences, correcting any errors in the use of abbreviations. If a sentence is already correct, write *C*.

Example 1. We arrived at 831 S. Highland Ave. at exactly 6:30 A.M. in the morning.

We arrived at 831 South Highland Avenue at exactly 6: 30 A.M.
_____

11. Sen. Johnson made his statement on Tues., Jan. 25.

_____

12. By 9:00 P.M. the rainfall total was three inches.

_____

13. Today's speaker is Dr. Olivia Ortega, M.D.

_____

14. The painting is thirty-eight in. wide and twenty in. high.

_____

15. Andrew Jackson Young, Junior, was mayor of Atlanta, GA, from 1981 to 1989.

_____

16. Will Mister Brooks be joining us for the concert?

_____

17. The kingdom of Kush lasted from about 2000 B.C. until about A.D. 350.

_____

18. Meet me at 82 W. Woodson St. at 7:30 P.M. in the evening.

_____

19. Ms. Jee recently visited Koreatown in Los Angeles, California.

_____

20. This pottery dates back to about B.C. 300.

_____

C. CORRECTING SENTENCES BY ADDING COMMAS Insert commas where they are needed in the following sentences. If a sentence is already correct, write *C* on the line provided.

Example _____ **1.** I think that Marta**,** Tony**,** and Jeb will take the last train**,** which leaves at 9:00.

_____ **21.** When our doorbell rings the dog barks the cat hides and the parakeet screeches.

_____ **22.** Lindsey's acceptance letter was signed "Sincerely Gladys Epps Ph.D."

_____ **23.** Ed or Joel or Maurice will help set up chairs in the gymnasium.

_____ **24.** Well Marcus are you coming with us or not?

_____ **25.** The island of Puerto Rico which boasts a pleasant climate and beautiful beaches attracts many tourists.

_____ **26.** According to the rules of soccer the goalkeeper is the only player who is allowed to touch the ball with his or her hands.

_____ **27.** Mount St. Helens a volcano near Seattle Washington erupted on May 18 1980.

_____ **28.** A wolf can eat up to twenty pounds of food at one time but it can also go without food for more than two weeks.

_____ **29.** In fact a strong tornado can uproot a large tree overturn a railroad car or carry a pickup truck hundreds of meters.

_____ **30.** Please make some tacos for lunch Rosita.

_____ **31.** Turtles that live on land have domelike shells and heavy short clublike legs and feet.

_____ **32.** Melissa has a part-time job at the camera shop yet she still makes excellent grades in all of her classes.

_____ **33.** Did you know by the way that Alberto Ríos will be speaking at the university tonight?

_____ **34.** Our cross-country journey took us across deserts over mountains and through majestic woodlands.

_____ **35.** Any belongings left in the locker room will be taken to the lost and found box.

_____ **36.** On the way to the park we met Jenna Davies who moved to our neighborhood about two weeks ago.

_____ **37.** Reggie Johnson hoping for a second chance asked Coach Chancellor to put him in the game.

_____ **38.** Abigail did her report on Daniel James Jr. the first African American four-star general in United States history.

_____ **39.** Matthew missed the layup but made the free throw.

_____ **40.** Held each August the snake dance of the Hopi lasts nine days.

D. PROOFREADING FOR THE CORRECT USE OF END MARKS AND COMMAS Each of the following sentences contains at least one error in the use of end marks or commas. Correct each sentence by inserting end marks and commas where needed and by crossing out any unnecessary commas or end marks.

Example 1. Gymnastics, which has been an Olympic sport for more than a century, is widely covered on TV.

41. My gymnastics class meets at 7:00 PM., on Wednesdays.

42. The Herndon Youth Gymnastics Center located at 151 Pine Street has all the finest equipment.

43. Our instructor Mr Talbot is an accomplished athlete, and an excellent teacher.

44. Whenever I have trouble with a routine he offers assistance patience and encouragement

45. The parallel bars are my favorite event but I also like, the horse vault, and the rings

46. I work hard on every event of course.

47. When will I finally perfect my dismount, from the horizontal bar

48. Aaron Jackson one of the best athletes in the class can do a handstand, on the parallel bars

49. What an incredible feat, that is

50. This fun challenging sport, helps me develop endurance flexibility and strength.

Punctuation: Semicolons and Colons

A. USING SEMICOLONS CORRECTLY IN SENTENCES   Each of the following sentences needs to have at least one semicolon inserted. Some semicolons need to be inserted where there is no punctuation; others need to be inserted in place of a comma. Insert each semicolon, and use a caret (∧) to show where the semicolon goes.

Example 1. Penguins swim below the surface of the water; consequently, they need to surface

about once every minute for air.

1. I gazed out the window and surveyed the snow-covered lawn the beauty of the winter won-
derland seemed to beckon me.

2. I would like to thank my parents, who encouraged me, my husband, who held my hand, and
my dear friend Sally, who believed in the dream.

3. My aunt and uncle did not go to Arizona this year instead, they went to San Francisco for the
Chinese New Year celebration.

4. Pablo likes to read mystery novels and science fiction, his brother prefers nonfiction.

5. After breakfast I went outside with my mother, my sister, and my cousin, and Mom, who
loves snow, helped us build a snow sculpture.

6. Sara and I took Roberto to the movies, meanwhile, Mr. and Mrs. Sanchez were decorating the
basement for the surprise party.

7. Tamika finished her chores early she wanted to get to the pool by noon.

8. Mr. Ned Durand, an environmentalist, Ms. Linda O'Toole, a developer, and Mrs. Gloria
Shapiro, a concerned citizen, will attend the city council meeting.

9. Guadalupe Day is an important Mexican holiday it honors the patron saint of Mexico, the
Virgin of Guadalupe.

10. In folklore and fairy tales, wolves have often been portrayed as evil and aggressive, for
example, in "Little Red Riding Hood" a wolf tries to eat a little girl.

B. CORRECTING SENTENCES BY ADDING COLONS   Insert colons where they are needed in the following sentences. Circle the colons you add. If a sentence does not need a colon, write *C* on the line provided.

Example _____ **1.** Taking the podium, Dr. Chu had this to say: "People of Huntsville, on this
day our community faces a unique challenge."

_____ **11.** Emily was proud of her sculpture She displayed it on the mantel for all to see.

_____ **12.** To make this type of sushi, you will need the following ingredients vinegared rice, imitation crab, and cucumber.

_____ **13.** Aunt Lydia reminded me of these words by Benjamin E. Mays "The tragedy of life does not lie in not reaching your goal. The tragedy lies in having no goal to reach."

_____ **14.** If you are going to the supermarket, please look for canned chickpeas, romaine lettuce, and fresh garlic.

_____ **15.** The order of speakers will be as follows Mr. Theodore Huston, Mrs. Yolando Moore, and Mr. Bill Jennings.

_____ **16.** The following morning the mayor made a public statement "Ladies and gentlemen, today is a sad day for me. Due to a serious illness in my family, I must regrettably resign as your mayor."

_____ **17.** The list of authors our teacher gave us for our class reports includes Jade Snow Wong, Richard Kim, and Frank Chin.

_____ **18.** The instructions of the museum guide were very clear Stay with the group, and don't touch anything.

_____ **19.** At the assembly Principal Hunt welcomed the freshmen and other new students "To those of you who are new here this year, let me say I believe in the potential of each one of you and wish you great success here at Spring Grove High."

_____ **20.** The article describes the three types of conga drums the quinto, the conga, and the tumbadora.

C. USING COLONS IN CONVENTIONAL SITUATIONS   On the line provided, rewrite each of the following items, inserting colons where they are needed.

Example 1. beginning at 5 15 P.M.   _____*beginning at 5:15 P.M.*_____

21. Genesis 3 2   _____

22. the 9 15 train   _____

23. Dear Senator Howell   _____

24. James 3 7–11   _____

25. Please call before 8 00 A.M.   _____

26. *Hattie The Life of Hattie McDaniel*   _____

27. 9 30 in the evening _____

28. Dear Ms. Fernandez _____

29. *Friendly Islands A History of Tonga* _____

30. "Turtles Creatures of Land and Sea" _____

D. PROOFREADING FOR THE CORRECT USE OF SEMICOLONS AND COLONS Correct each of the following sentences by adding semicolons and colons where they are needed. Use a caret (∧) to show where each semicolon or colon should go.

Example 1. Mr. Stinson gave us the following directions ∧ at the top of the page, write your name, date, and test number ∧ and beginning with Part A, answer as many of the test items as possible.

31. The concert, which will last from 8 00 to 11 00, will feature the following types of music jazz, reggae, rap, and gospel.

32. The local Humane Society is a nonprofit organization, therefore, it relies heavily on donations and on volunteers.

33. I invited Joni, Charles, and Linda and Latoya, my sister, invited three of her friends.

34. At 10 30, Reverend McKay began the sermon with a reading of I Samuel 17 20–50.

35. During the first part of our trip, we drove through these cities Hartford, Connecticut, Providence, Rhode Island, and Lowell, Massachusetts.

36. Some bats use their senses of sight and smell to navigate, others rely on echoes.

37. Waiting patiently for our 5 45 flight, we learned it had been delayed until 7 15.

38. Dr. Hanover presented leadership awards to Bianca Williams, class president, Lian Cho, captain of the girls' soccer team, and Damon Hill, head of the debate team.

39. The movie started at 7 30, it was not over until 10 15.

40. Being on the track team demands much of my free time, on the other hand, I enjoy the exercise and have made several close friends on the team.

Punctuation: Italics and Quotation Marks

A. USING UNDERLINING (ITALICS) CORRECTLY IN SENTENCES Underline the word or words that should be italicized in each of the following sentences.

Example 1. The community theater will produce both Fences and Driving Miss Daisy next year.

1. Among the sleek, streamlined passenger trains that were put into operation in the 1930s was the City of Salina.

2. Cameron can never remember whether tomorrow is spelled with one r or two.

3. The Living Is Easy and The Wedding are both novels by Dorothy West.

4. In an old issue of the York Daily Record, I found a review of the movie Dances with Wolves.

5. Traveling from Georgia to England in 1819, the Savannah became the first steamship to cross the Atlantic Ocean.

6. Several United States coins bear the motto e pluribus unum, which means "out of many, one."

7. The Hubble Space Telescope was repaired by astronauts from the space shuttle Endeavour.

8. Two of Kerry's favorite works of art are Emancipation, a lithograph by Phoebe Beasley, and Crossing the Bridge, an oil painting by John Biggers.

9. Melinda needs to work on her handwriting; her h's look like r's, and her s's look like 5's.

10. Aunt Gertie went to see Einstein on the Beach, an opera by Philip Glass and Robert Wilson.

B. PUNCTUATING SENTENCES BY ADDING QUOTATION MARKS AND OTHER MARKS OF PUNCTUATION In the following sentences, insert quotation marks, single quotation marks, and other marks of punctuation where they are needed. Circle any lowercase letters that should be capital letters. If a sentence is correct, write C on the line provided.

Example _____ **1.** Didn't Ms. Osaka say, " research several different American Indian crafts " ?

_____ **11.** Look at the bowls in this picture, said Ethan they are shaped like animals.

_____ **12.** Were those made by Indians of the Mississippi Valley asked Juanita.

_____ **13.** Ms. Osaka said that the Inca were excellent potters.

_____ **14.** Jeff, did you say hand me the book on the Northwest Coast Indians Mia asked.

_____ **15.** Jeff told the others that the wooden masks carved by the Indians of the Northwest Coast actually had movable parts.

_____ **16.** I think said Ethan they also carved totem poles.

_____ **17.** Mia exclaimed here's an article titled Sand Paintings of the Pueblo

_____ **18.** The Navajo remarked Jeff are famous for their beautiful wool blankets and rugs.

_____ **19.** Juanita explained that some peoples in the Lake Superior area crafted tools, weapons,

and decorative items from copper.

_____ **20.** The basketry of the Pomo is really impressive said Ethan their baskets could actually

hold water.

C. PUNCTUATING DIALOGUE BY ADDING QUOTATION MARKS Add quotation marks and single quotation marks where they are needed in the following dialogue. Insert a paragraph symbol (¶) wherever a new paragraph should begin.

Example **[1]** " Have you chosen a poet for your English paper? " Monica asked Chad. **[2]** ¶" I'm

thinking about Sandra Cisneros, " Chad answered. " I have always liked her poems. "

[21] Oh, yes, said Monica, Sandra Cisneros is one of my favorites, too. I haven't read much

about her life, though. **[22]** Well, Chad responded, she didn't have an easy life. She grew up in

Chicago in a large working-class family.

[23] Don't many of her works draw on her childhood experiences? asked Monica. **[24]** Yes, said

Chad, she has written powerful poems and stories about the tough sections of Chicago and about

the circumstances of kids like her. **[25]** Her Mexican American heritage is shown in her writing,

too, and she incorporates elements of the Spanish language.

[26] You've really done your homework, Monica said. What else can you tell me? **[27]** Well,

Chad replied, Cisneros is a gifted teacher as well as a terrific poet. **[28]** Now, that's something I

didn't know, said Monica. What are your favorite Cisneros poems? **[29]** It's hard to name a

favorite, Chad answered, but the poems Muddy Kid Comes Home and Six Brothers come to

mind. **[30]** I think you'll get a good grade on that English paper, said Monica.

D. PROOFREADING SENTENCES FOR THE CORRECT USE OF UNDERLINING (ITALICS) AND QUOTATION MARKS Insert quotation marks and single quotation marks where they are needed in the following sentences. Underline each word that should be in italics. If a sentence is already correct, write *C* on the line provided.

Example _____ **1.** " Have you read <u>Roots: The Saga of an American Family?</u> " asked Ryan.

_____ **31.** In Puerto Rico, Mr. Foster explained, children receive gifts on Three Kings' Day.

_____ **32.** Please use the words reassurance and loyalty in original sentences, requested

Mrs. Lopez.

_____ **33.** Lola warned me, You heard Mom. She said, Don't go anywhere until I get back.

_____ **34.** The Normandie, a luxurious French ocean liner, was destroyed by fire in 1942.

_____ **35.** Paul Laurence Dunbar's poem Sympathy appears in his first poetry collection, Oak

and Ivy.

_____ **36.** The children's TV show Sesame Street features the Muppets, which were created by

puppeteer Jim Henson.

_____ **37.** I believe I've decided on a title for my poem, announced Jalene. How does Sands and

Shells sound to you?

_____ **38.** Victor yelled, Watch out for that tree!

_____ **39.** Constantin Brancusi created Flying Turtle, which is one of Kaitlin's favorite sculptures.

_____ **40.** Pat said that both Apollo 16 and Apollo 17 landed on the moon in 1972.

_____ **41.** Michelle said, Mr. Katz told me that in 2006 Alex Rodriguez was the highest-paid

professional baseball player.

_____ **42.** Is that a 2 or a 3 at the end of your phone number?

_____ **43.** Is it true, asked Kent, that Neil Simon's play Lost in Yonkers won a Pulitzer Prize?

_____ **44.** I wish, she said, that I could visit Guatemala one day.

_____ **45.** A charreada, or Mexican rodeo, is usually more dangerous than an American rodeo.

_____ **46.** How many Secret Service agents accompany the President on Air Force One?

_____ **47.** Isamu Noguchi was famous for his sculpture, Mrs. Starbird explained. He also

designed furniture and helped plan gardens, playgrounds, and bridges.

_____ **48.** Alicia continued, Then Aunt Susie shouted, Don't touch that! It's hot!

_____ **49.** For tomorrow please read the article Women in Astronomy and the essay Waiting for

Freedom, said Mr. Hena.

_____ **50.** At the free concert, the Metropolitan Youth Chorus sang a variety of folk songs,

including Old Chisholm Trail and We Shall Overcome.

Punctuation: Apostrophes

A. **USING APOSTROPHES TO FORM THE POSSESSIVE CASE OF NOUNS** On the line provided, revise each of the following items by using the possessive case.

Example **1.** a truck belonging to the Acme Repair Company

the Acme Repair Company's truck

1. the performance of the singer

_____

2. the room of my brothers

_____

3. the staff of Southside Animal Hospital

_____

4. the bicycle belonging to Theo and the bicycle belonging to Kevin

_____

5. an article by the scientist

_____

6. a computer shared by Peter and Todd

_____

7. the job of the parole officer

_____

8. bowling shoes belonging to Mr. Saunders

_____

9. clothing for women

_____

10. a house belonging to the Jeffersons

_____

B. **CHOOSING THE CORRECT FORMS OF NOUNS AND PRONOUNS** Underline the correct word in parentheses in each of the following sentences.

Example **1.** "The bird will be (_ours, our's_)," said Branford, "and (_well, we'll_) both take care of it."

11. My brother Branford had been saving (_his, his'_) money for (_month's, months_) to buy a bird, and I was going to help him take care of it.

ELEMENTS OF LANGUAGE | Third Course

12. Branford and I read a book about pet (*birds, birds'*) and then went to examine (*Pet Emporiums, Pet Emporium's*) selection.

13. (*Everyone's, Everyones*) preferences are different when it comes to (*pets, pet's*).

14. You can benefit from getting (*another's, anothers*) advice before making (*your, you're*) decision.

15. Branford likes the (*parrots, parrots'*) because (*they're, their*) able to talk and do tricks.

16. However, since a large (*parrots, parrot's*) life span can be over fifty (*years, years'*), caring for one is a big commitment.

17. (*Its, It's*) not easy to provide the proper diet for these (*birds, birds'*), either.

18. If (*your, you're*) looking for a less demanding (*species, species'*), you might consider a parakeet, a canary, or a zebra finch.

19. (*Wed, We'd*) looked closely at a male canary, (*whose, who's*) beautiful singing enchanted us both.

20. The (*parakeet's, parakeets'*) sociability won us over in the end, and we picked a fancy green one with yellow patches on (*its, it's*) wings.

C. CORRECTING SENTENCES BY ADDING APOSTROPHES Insert apostrophes where they are needed in the following sentences. If a sentence is already correct, write *C* on the line provided.

Example _____ **1.** Let's exchange drafts of our papers for Mrs. Wheeler's class and give each other feedback.

_____ **21.** Angela read my composition, and I read hers.

_____ **22.** Weve often helped each other with papers by offering constructive criticism.

_____ **23.** I dont have many mechanical problems, but my organizational abilities arent the best.

_____ **24.** Since I cant tell *l*s from *i*s or *r*s from *s*s when I read Angelas handwriting, she always types her drafts on the computer.

_____ **25.** I pointed out that her paper had too many *and*s and *so*s.

_____ **26.** Luckily, ours is a solid friendship, and we do not get upset about these little critiques.

_____ **27.** Angela, whose English grades are usually As and Bs, helped me organize my paper and improve its style.

_____ **28.** She recommended that I replace some of my *then*s with different transitional words.

_____ **29.** Have you tried getting another classmates feedback on your writing assignments?

_____ **30.** I havent known many other students who help each other as much as Angela and I do, but Im sure that anyones writing could be improved by getting such feedback.

D. PROOFREADING SENTENCES FOR THE CORRECT USE OF APOSTROPHES In the following sentences, apostrophes are either missing or incorrectly used. Draw a line through each incorrect word, and write the correct form above it.

Example 1. I'd like to meet you before the ~~Levines~~ *Levines'* party if ~~your~~ *you're* available.

31. For many years' the Westminster Kennel Clubs big dog show has been held at Madison Square Garden every February.

32. Mrs. Martinez will spend her two weeks vacation in the Dominican Republic and Haiti.

33. The rain leaked through the seam's of the tent, and Reggies and Alans gear got soaked.

34. The players bodies were tired and sore, but they're spirits were high.

35. Jupiters mass is 318 times that of the Earth, but it's density is relatively low.

36. I don't like this typeface; I cant tell the *8*s from the *&*s.

37. The Toltec Indian's built the big, stepped pyramid at Cholula.

38. Was someones car parked in front of the Andersons house all night?

39. Are these tortilla warmers yours or their's?

40. No ones burritos' are tastier than hers.

41. I promise you that well be sure to invite Alex to go with us since he is a friend of your's.

42. In the United States of America, a fair trial is everyones right.

43. Debbie and Jamie's presentation is first; our's comes after theirs'.

44. The museums exhibit of paintings by contemporary American Indian artist's opens tomorrow.

45. My teachers suggestion was that I revise some sentences to reduce the number of *becauses* in my essay.

46. Thurgood Marshalls appointment to the U.S. Supreme Court in 1967 was a historic event.

47. The Brontë sisters joint volume of poems was published under the pen names Currer, Ellis, and Acton Bell.

48. Visit the Parks and Wildlife Departments Web site to find out about registering your canoe.

49. My friend Lisa, whose looking for the perfect gift for her sister-in-laws birthday, asked my advice.

50. The childrens faces lit up when Mr. Guerro entered with a colorful, elephant-shaped piñata.

Punctuation: Hyphens, Dashes, Parentheses, Brackets, Ellipsis Points

A. USING HYPHENS TO DIVIDE WORDS AT THE ENDS OF LINES On the line provided, write each of the following words, using a hyphen to indicate where the word may be divided at the end of a line. If a word should not be divided, write *do not divide*.

Example 1. industry _____ *in-dus-try* _____

1. absolutely _____

2. correct _____

3. three-year-olds _____

4. humming _____

5. subtraction _____

6. alert _____

7. confidence _____

8. judgment _____

9. brought _____

10. historical _____

B. USING HYPHENS, PARENTHESES, AND DASHES CORRECTLY IN SENTENCES Insert hyphens, parentheses, and dashes to punctuate the following sentences correctly. Use a caret (∧) to indicate where each punctuation mark should go. Do not add commas to these sentences.

Example 1. Dr. Joel Whitehead ∧an ex∧Marine medic∧ was the speaker at the banquet.

11. The forensics team is well prepared for the tournament to be held in midOctober.

12. The dining room it's very dimly lit is not the best room for reading or for sewing.

13. Mrs. Chisholm she's an expert in African mythology, you know told us that the Ashantis con sider rivers to be extremely sacred.

14. "Have you seen my" Coreen began as the phone rang.

15. During the Classic Period of the Maya civilization about A.D. 250 to A.D. 900, the Maya made great achievements in the arts.

16. Stephanie said, "Twenty six coins in my collection wow, that's almost one half of my entire collection are very rare."

17. My uncle Harold retired for three years now worked at an art museum that specialized in preColumbian sculpture.

18. The president elect of the university promised well constructed wheelchair ramps and other improvements to all campus buildings.

19. Many people fear or dislike bats, but these animals actually perform a valuable service they eat insects.

20. Add one quarter teaspoon dried basil and one half cup water.

21. A two thirds majority of the student council at least twenty one members is required to pass the motion.

22. The Indian sign language was developed after new groups the Arapaho, the Cheyenne, the Sioux, and others moved to the Great Plains.

23. Self discipline is an all important trait for any self employed person who wants to be a success.

24. The collection includes stories by twenty eight well known writers.

25. Barbara Jordan 1936–1996 was the first African American to give the keynote address at a Democratic national convention.

26. That company it sells mostly housewares now offers shopping over the Internet.

27. Gloria Estefan one of Callie's favorite singers is appearing on a TV special Saturday night.

28. Timothy announced, "The secret is no, I guess I really shouldn't tell you yet."

29. The Bayonne Bridge, which connects Staten Island and New Jersey, is 1,675 feet 511 meters long.

30. Mr. Bernstein explained the significance of the major Jewish pilgrimage festivals Passover, Shavuot, and Sukkot.

C. USING HYPHENS, PARENTHESES, DASHES, ELLIPSIS POINTS, AND BRACKETS CORRECTLY IN SENTENCES

Proofread each of the following sentences for the correct use of hyphens, parentheses, dashes, ellipsis points, and brackets. Cross out any incorrect punctuation marks, and insert punctuation where needed. Do not change or add commas, end marks, or quotation marks. Use a caret (∧) to indicate where each punctuation mark should go. If a sentence is correct, write *C* on the line provided.

Example _____ 1. The exgovernor ended his speech by saying, "I'm sure that Mr. Murphy head of the cleanup effort will have his team ready in no time . . . and that the park will be sparkling clean well before the deadline."

_____ 31. Some American Indian and African instruments conga drums, maracas, marimbas, claves are used in Cuban music.

_____ 32. A beautifully-decorated vase (Japanese, I think adorned the wooden end table.

ELEMENTS OF LANGUAGE | Third Course

_____ **33.** Sergeant Fallon was quoted as saying, "The suspect was questioned at (the Drybend Police Department) Headquarters on Monday afternoon and was then released."

_____ **34.** The shuttle takeoff could be rescheduled for as early as Tuesday morning wait, make that Wednesday morning.

_____ **35.** Wendy, an ex-cheerleader, is now concentrating seriously on gymnastics and diving.

_____ **36.** On the twenty sixth of November, Grandma Goodlive will be seventy seven years old.

_____ **37.** Was Chelsea's great grandmother really a world-renowned physicist?

_____ **38.** "No! Don't close the—" Vinny began, but it was too late.

_____ **39.** Ernesto Galarza [1905–1984] was a historian and writer who worked to further the civil rights of Mexican Americans.

_____ **40.** The mayor stated, "This event (the Memorial Day Parade) is a Maryville tradition, and I do not intend to let it fade."

_____ **41.** The directions for this exercise say, "Proofread . . . for the correct use of hyphens, parentheses, dashes, ellipsis points, and brackets."

_____ **42.** Most population centers are near the coastline. (See page 142 (Map 2) for more detail.)

_____ **43**. Wynton Marsalis he's my favorite jazz musician was once a member of Art Blakey's Jazz Messengers.

_____ **44.** Most of the large beads—the ones in this box can be used for earrings or necklaces.

_____ **45.** Our science book defines *virus* as "a simple, microscopic organism that . . . . can cause disease in another organism by damaging some of its cells."

_____ **46.** My term paper, which came to almost twenty one pages, was well-researched and I think well-written.

_____ **47.** During the second semester the class will focus on postRenaissance Italian literature.

_____ **48.** "Well," the witness stammered, "I couldn't quite see . . . . . . too dark in the stairwell."

_____ **49.** One half of the entire length of the thresher shark (20 feet [6.1 meters]) consists of the animal's enormous tail.

_____ **50.** The fact is as if I even need to tell you this the city is growing too quickly.

Spelling: Improving Your Spelling

A. PROOFREADING SENTENCES TO CORRECT SPELLING ERRORS   Most of the following sentences contain errors in spelling or in the use of numbers. Cross out each error, and write the word correctly above the misspelled word. If a sentence is already correct, write *C* on the line provided.

Example   _____   **1.** Mr. Sheng, who is very ~~knowledgable~~ *knowledgeable* about environmental science, ~~explainned~~ *explained* the importance of rain forests.

_____   **1.** Uncle Ramon has pilotted more than two hundred flights since he got his license 3 years ago.

_____   **2.** It took the three of us nearly all Saturday afternoon to finish raking the leafs in the backyard.

_____   **3.** We had to wait fifteen minutes at the crossing while the freight train passed.

_____   **4.** Still a beginer, Sam sometimes has difficulty controling the mountain bike.

_____   **5.** At the ceremony 15 outstanding seniors recieved awards.

_____   **6.** After slumberring several hours, the toddlers playyed until dinnertime.

_____   **7.** The Spanish rice was beautifuly garnished with diced tomatos.

_____   **8.** To everyone's relief, the theif was finally caught.

_____   **9.** Dr. Martin Luther King, Jr., was a courageous civil rights leader.

_____   **10.** My older sister is saveing her money and hopes to buy a relyable car soon.

_____   **11.** In March the Jee family moved for the 4th time in 6 years.

_____   **12.** Not only did John succeed, but he exceded everyone's expectations.

_____   **13.** The day-care classes, made up mostly of four-year-olds, ran gleefully around the playground.

_____   **14.** Council member Itoh made an announcment today that surprised many people.

_____   **15.** The Lopezes and the Owenses are active members of the nieghborhood crime-watch group.

_____   **16.** 78 students attended the Cuban Dance Festival.

_____   **17.** Dr. Garcia first checked the child's height and weight.

_____   **18.** Traceing her family tree back four generations, Libby learned that she has ancestors from Spain.

_____   **19.** Toby has two brothers-in-laws, and both are from Idaho.

_____ **20.** Many a tourist has spent days shoping at the craft stores and markets lining the

avenue.

_____ **21.** Overcome with greif and a feeling of emptyness, Daniel asked for some time alone.

_____ **22.** Residents are hopeful that the floodwaters will recede quickly.

_____ **23.** The children enjoyed feeding the gooses and watching the butterflys.

_____ **24.** Amy forced a smile, but she knew it lookked unatural.

_____ **25.** According to the advertisment, all stereoes are on sale this week.

B. DISTINGUISHING BETWEEN WORDS OFTEN CONFUSED   Underline the correct word in each set of parentheses in the following sentences.

Example 1. Martin interviewed the marketing director, (*who's*, *whose*) (*principal*, *principle*) duties

include advertising and package design.

26. Has the new guidance (*councilor*, *counselor*) been (*formally*, *formerly*) introduced to all the

teachers?

27. Didn't you (*hear*, *here*) those construction trucks when they (*passed*, *past*) by?

28. Yes, storm chasing is exciting work, but (*its*, *it's*) (*quiet*, *quite*) dangerous.

29. How will this high-pressure system (*affect*, *effect*) the (*weather*, *whether*) in the northern part of

the state?

30. Begin with a square (*peace*, *piece*) of (*plain*, *plane*) cloth.

31. Mrs. Alvarez has (*all ready*, *already*) raised the (*capital*, *capitol*) needed to start her software

company.

32. I temporarily lost my way (*to*, *too*) Uncle Jason's house, but now I am back on (*coarse*, *course*).

33. Did you receive any (*complements*, *compliments*) on (*your*, *you're*) new haircut?

34. Some people strive to reach a higher (*plain*, *plane*) of awareness (*threw*, *through*) meditation.

35. The article discusses the harmful (*affects*, *effects*) of excessive sunbathing and says that it is

never (*alright*, *all right*) to spend much time in the sun without sunscreen.

36. He sometimes offers more (*advice*, *advise*) (*than*, *then*) I really want.

37. Mom is able to exercise indoors by riding her (*stationary*, *stationery*) bicycle in all kinds of

(*weather*, *whether*).

38. The Kwanzaa holiday is based upon seven (*principals*, *principles*) of African American culture

and lasts a (*weak*, *week*).

39. The puppies are still (*to, too, two*) (*weak, week*) to stand up.

40. Write on both sides so you won't (*waist, waste*) any of this beautiful (*stationary, stationery*).

41. The poor condition of the (*brakes, breaks*) made the car (*all together, altogether*) unsafe.

42. Classic movies are (*shone, shown*) (*their, there*) in the summer.

43. (*Weather, Whether*) you follow your attorney's (*council, counsel*) is entirely up to you.

44. A firm belief in (*peace, piece*) is part of his (*moral, morale*) code.

45. Is the dress (*loose, lose*) enough around the (*waist, waste*)?

46. Our (*moral, morale*) improved after Coach Thomson (*lead, led*) our team to a thrilling victory over the Panthers.

47. Some animals that live near (*hear, here*) in the (*desert, dessert*) are inactive, or dormant, during the summer.

48. I (*advice, advise*) you to (*altar, alter*) your plan before it is too late.

49. The committee (*choose, chose*) Dr. Thelma Jefferson, (*formally, formerly*) a Navy pilot, to direct the new program.

50. Finish your peas, and (*than, then*) you may have (*desert, dessert*).

Correcting Common Errors

A. CORRECTING USAGE ERRORS IN SENTENCES   Draw a line through the incorrect word or words in each of the following sentences. Then, write the correct word or words above each error.

Example 1. The snake finally turned its head and ~~slithers~~ *slithered* away from my brother and ~~I~~ *me*.

1. The people in this family really enjoys our summer camping trips.

2. I think Mom is more at ease outdoors then anyone in my family.

3. Dad and Theo usually put up both of the tents, but Mom and me are the experts at gathering wood and building campfires.

4. Mom don't enjoy fishing herself, but she is happy to help we anglers clean and prepare our catch for dinner.

5. We never hike a long ways from camp without we are carrying a compass.

6. One of my favorite camping activities are photographing wildlife.

7. Last summer I taked my camera along and got some real good photos of a number of different type of birds.

8. After I developed the photos, I use my field guide to identify each species.

9. Each of my brothers has their own way of enjoying the outdoors.

10. Both Bobby and Theo loves an adventure, but Theo is probably the most daring of the two.

11. The only family member who has ever been bitten by a snake is him.

12. My terriblest camping mishap could of been avoided if I had been more carefuller.

13. Stopping to rest during a strenuous hike, I set down right in the middle of a huge patch of poison ivy.

14. Before I known it, my arms and legs were on fire with itching.

15. My father, whom is a physician's assistant, begins treating the outbreak as soon as I returned to camp.

16. Five days are too long to suffer with that type of skin irritation!

17. Mom buyed my brothers and I new sleeping bags two years ago.

18. Beside tents and sleeping bags, cooking equipment and first-aid supplies are a must on camping trips.

19. I never get tired of laying in the tent at night, listening to the sounds of nature.

20. We usually cook over a campfire, and most of the food taste well.

B. CORRECTING MECHANICS ERRORS IN SENTENCES Each of the following sentences contains at least one error in capitalization, punctuation, or spelling. Draw a line through each error, and write the correct word or punctuation mark in the space above the error. In some cases you will simply need to add or delete punctuation. Use a caret (∧) to show exactly where each punctuation mark should go. Underline any words that should be in italics.

Example 1. Roger had ~~carefuly~~ *carefully* prepared his presentation on the ~~battle~~ *Battle* of ~~gettysburg,~~ *Gettysburg;* nevertheless he was nervous when his turn came.

21. The following art museums are located in Washington D C; the freer gallery of art, the Arthur

M Sackler gallery, and the national museum of african art.

22. While in Philadelphia, the bradford family visited fairmount park thats one of the largest city

parks in the United States.

23. My dog does several tricks, for example he can shake hands roll over and beg.

24. how long has Thomas been rehearseing for this audition

25. Next semester i will be taking physics I, geometry, and spanish.

26. Before you have the invitation's printed, make sure you can reserve the dance hall for

saturday November 15.

27. The wilsons have lived in several different citys Kansas City Missouri, San Diego California,

and Baltimore, Maryland.

28. Marcus wrote an insightful analysis of marigolds a short story by eugenia collier.

29. Mrs. Brooks asked is anyone familiar with N Scott Momadays novel house made of Dawn.

30. Sallys 2nd motion passed by a two thirds majority and the president Nathan Ramirez pro

ceded to the next order of business.

31. Have you seen my oh, there it is, said Kristen.

32. The diet satisfyed all dayly nutritional needs but their seemed to be something missing.

33. Made of a course fabric, the robes scratched the choir members necks.

34. In a lecture at the community college dr ramirez described the asteroid belt between mars and

jupiter and explained how it was formed.

35. Both teams anchor runers were fast, but our's sprintted across the finish line first.

36. Bill Cosby's warm gentle humor has made him a highly popular entertainer he has also

written several books

37. Karens surprise party which lasted from 7 30 until 10 00 was fun for everyone.

38. Isnt the poem A narrow fellow in the grass about a snake

39. Hey Watch out for that ditch yelled the Sergeant.

40. Angela please hand me that hammer, and a couple of nailes

C. PROOFREADING A LETTER FOR CORRECT USAGE AND MECHANICS Each numbered item in the following business letter contains at least one error in usage or mechanics. Correct each error by crossing out the incorrect word or punctuation mark and writing your correction in the space above the error. Underline any word that should be in italics, and use a caret (‸) to show where each punctuation mark goes.

Example [1] Please send my parents and ~~t~~a refund *me* we will appreciate your prompt reply.

[41] Mary Anne Billings

424 mountain view road

Roanoke VA 24020-1688

May 17 2002

[42] Mildred Jackson PhD

Hollins university

P O Box 9657

Roanoke VA 24020-1688

[43] dear dr jackson

[44] My book club the southside readers is organizing a seminar, on the evening of thursday july 16 2002. [45] Several of our members has read your reviews in the Virginia Literary Journal and wed like to extend an invitation to you to join our panel.

[46] The topic for the panel discussion will be a specialty of your's african american folklore.

[47] The club have decided to focus on Zora Neale Hurstons book Mules And Men.

[48] Please contact me by April 6 to let us know weather or not you will be able to join us.

[49] It would be a delight for the other members and I if you would except this invitation.

[50] sincerely

Mary Anne Billing

Mary Anne Billings

Writing Complete Sentences

IDENTIFYING SENTENCE FRAGMENTS

DIRECTIONS Some of the following word groups are sentence fragments. First, identify which are fragments and which are complete sentences. Second, identify what is missing in each sentence fragment, using the instructions that follow. Then, revise each fragment by making it a complete sentence.

- If the item is a complete sentence, write C next to the item number.
- If a subject is missing, write S.
- If a verb is missing, write V.
- If both a subject and a verb are missing, write SV.
- If the item has a subject and verb but does not express a complete thought, write N.

Example __S__ **1.** last night read a book about an adventure.

_____ **1.** two elves, a unicorn, and a knight

_____ **2.** under a huge, ancient oak tree

_____ **3.** because an evil wizard had put a curse on him

_____ **4.** to find the golden key to the crystal tower

_____ **5.** searched the kingdom

_____ **6.** who explored caves and mountain tops

_____ **7.** they looked over the edge of the world

_____ **8.** two enormous lions

_____ **9.** after a long journey to search

_____ **10.** a roller coaster, a pack of talking dogs, and a seventy-foot-tall chicken

_____ **11.** the sun shining through the colorful clouds

_____ **12.** the legend of the dragon amazed the warrior

_____ **13.** soared into the night with a burst of fire

_____ **14.** although they could not understand the secret words

_____ **15.** with an anxious heart and shaking hands

_____ **16.** that addressed the princess and her two handmaidens

_____ **17.** graciously asking the wizard's permission

_____ **18.** a magical kingdom in the valley beneath the twin peaks

_____ **19.** in a clap of thunder, he arrived

_____ **20.** to surprise the people with a treasure chest

REVISING RUN-ON SENTENCES

DIRECTIONS The following items are run-on sentences. Revise each item either by making two complete sentences, or by making one compound sentence. Add words and change the punctuation and capitalization as necessary.

Example 21. For our last family vacation, we wanted to visit a
New England town with a rich history *; therefore,* we chose Concord,
Massachusetts.

21. Concord was settled in 1635, the name Concord reflected the town's friendly relations with American Indians.

22. The town played an important role in the American Revolution one of the first battles of the war was fought there.

23. The British came to seize the townspeople's weapons, the Minutemen met them at the North Bridge.

24. In a poem about the event, Ralph Waldo Emerson wrote about the gunfire at the bridge he called it "the shot heard round the world."

25. I had heard that phrase before, I didn't know anything about its history.

26. Concord also is important in the history of food, the Concord grape was developed there in the mid-1800s.

27. Most interesting to me, though, is the town's literary history, several of America's foremost nineteenth-century authors lived in Concord.

28. Nathaniel Hawthorne, Louisa May Alcott, and Henry David Thoreau all lived there, they are all buried in the same cemetery.

29. A number of historic homes are open to the public my family was able to visit Nathaniel Hawthorne's house and that of the Alcotts.

30. The Concord Museum has some great exhibits, it even has a collection of things from Ralph

Waldo Emerson's study.

REVISING FRAGMENTS AND RUN-ON SENTENCES

DIRECTIONS The following paragraphs contain several sentence fragments and run-on sentences. First, identify all fragments or run-ons. Then, revise them, adding words and changing the punctuation and capitalization as necessary to make each sentence clear and complete.

Example ~~Enjoy~~ *We enjoy* bowling and would like to know more about its history.

Bowling has not always existed in its current form. Dates back to 3200 B.C.

The Egyptians used stone pins and balls. To play the game.

In the Middle Ages, people played ninepins. The lanes were made of cin-

ders or clay, the pins were set up in a square. Skittles a variation of ninepins.

Is still played today in Great Britain.

The Dutch brought ninepins to the United States in the seventeenth

century. In the eighteenth century. A tenth pin was added to the game.

Bowling pins set by hand for many years. After the automatic pinsetter

was introduced in the 1950s. Many bowling alleys were built and the game

enjoyed a rebirth.

Today, bowling is still popular. Now the game is played on wooden lanes

with nonmetallic balls and wooden pins the pins are set in a triangle. Many

people enjoy. Playing in friendly games, local competitions, or championship

tournaments.

for **CHAPTER 19**   *page 488*   **CHAPTER TEST**

Writing Effective Sentences

COMBINING SENTENCES

DIRECTIONS   Combine each of the following sentences.

Example   1. Richard Wagner composed operas, ~~He composed operas~~ based

on Germanic legends.

1. Vincent van Gogh was an artist who painted during the 1800s. Vincent van Gogh was a

Dutch artist.

2. Alice Walker is a novelist, short-story writer, and poet. She is an African American.

3. Using charcoal, the artist sketched a portrait on a large tablet. The artist sketched skillfully.

4. The deer leaped suddenly into the shrubs. The deer was frightened by a loud noise.

5. Thomas Jefferson was the principal author of the Declaration of Independence. Thomas

Jefferson was a scholar and a skillful writer.

6. Frank Lloyd Wright designed the building for the Guggenheim Museum. The Guggenheim

Museum is in New York City.

7. Deep breathing is said to reduce the effects of stress. Relaxing thoughts are said to reduce the

effects of stress.

8. Sleep and exercise allow the body to recharge. They both help boost energy.

9. For several decades Germany was divided into two republics. The country was unified in

1990.

10. Some people want physicians to recommend alternative medicine remedies. Many medical

schools are offering more courses in alternative therapy.

11. Our school has new landscaping. The landscaping includes trees, flowers, and shrubs.

12. My teacher lets us discuss the front-page news each day. This keeps us knowledgeable about

current affairs.

IMPROVING SENTENCE STYLE

DIRECTIONS   The style of the following sentences needs to be improved.
Revise the sentences to make them clear and balanced. Use the headings
above each set of sentences to guide you.

Example   *Varying Sentence Beginnings:* Write your revisions on the line provided.

       13. Amy works at Pampered Paws because she loves grooming cats.

       Because she loves grooming cats, Amy works at Pampered Paws.

Using Parallel Structure: Use the space between items to make your revisions.

13. My friend Ian likes running, to jog, and swimming.

14. The supervisor explained that we needed four volunteers and to collect the club dues.

Revising Stringy Sentences: Use the space between items to make your revisions.

15. Lawrence Sullivan Ross was known as Sul Ross, and he was a state senator, and he was

    governor of Texas, and he lived in the 1800s.

16. Esther was supposed to play the lead in the play, but she came down with the flu, and then

    our teacher gave the role to Sara, but then Sara got sick, too, and now we have to find some-

    one else to play the lead.

Revising Wordy Sentences: Use the space between items to make your revisions.

17. Owing to the fact that I have a previous engagement, I will not be able to accompany you to

    the football game this Friday evening.

18. Might you possibly be able to find it in the goodness of your heart to assume my dog-walking

    responsibility this afternoon while I pay a visit to my dentist?

Varying Sentence Beginnings: Write your revisons on the lines provided.

19. Sojourner Truth was born a slave in New York, eventually gaining her freedom in 1828. She

    was an eloquent speaker on behalf of women and African Americans because she had a

    powerful voice and was a skillful orator.

    _____

    _____

20. Our class is planning a summer trip, so we plan to conduct fund-raising activities during the

    spring. We hope to have enough money for the trip by summer.

    _____

    _____

REVISING PARAGRAPHS

DIRECTIONS The following passage contains sentences that need to be improved. The parts that need to be revised are underlined. Using what you have learned, rewrite the five parts as you feel they should be written. Write your revisions on a separate sheet of paper.

Look for sentences that

- need to be combined
- are not parallel in structure
- are stringy or wordy
- lack varied beginnings

Example 21. Edison worked on a train that ran out of Detroit. He sold newspapers, sandwiches, and snacks.

Working on a train that ran out of Detroit, Edison sold newspapers, sandwiches, and snacks.

Thomas Alva Edison once described genius as a little bit of inspiration and a great deal of work. Whatever genius is, Edison had it. Most people consider him one of the greatest inventors in our country's history. He patented over one thousand inventions in sixty years.

(21) Edison had very little formal schooling. This was because his mother took him out of school at age seven. She was irritated because his schoolmaster thought Edison was stupid. Edison read widely, though, to make up for his lack of formal education.

Edison worked hard. **(22)** He was interested in many fields. He conducted experiments in fields ranging from medicine to farm relief. **(23)** Edison tried to develop devices that would work under usual conditions, be easy to repair, and that would not easily break.

(24) Edison was just twenty-one years old when he first took out a patent for an invention. The invention was an electric vote-recorder for counting votes made by legislators. Two years later, he repaired and improved a stock ticker, a telegraph device used to report the purchase and sale of stocks. With the money from the patents for the stock ticker, Edison opened his first workshop in Newark, New Jersey. **(25)** While in Newark, he improved the typewriter, and previously a person could usually write faster by hand than on the machine, and a few years later Edison moved his laboratory to Menlo Park, New Jersey. There he improved the telephone so that people no longer had to shout into the phone. The next year, Edison invented the phonograph, which is considered by many to be one of the world's most original inventions.

Understanding Paragraph Structure

PARAGRAPH STRUCTURE

DIRECTIONS Read the two paragraphs below and the passage on the following page. Then use what you have learned about paragraph structure to write answers to the items in the right column.

EXAMPLE

On Saturday, our class conducted a car wash to raise funds. Meanwhile, members of the senior class were staging a car wash of their own. Consequently, few people came to our car wash, and we raised little money.

1. Write one transition word or phrase used in this paragraph.

consequently

---

1. Write the topic sentence of Paragraph 1.

_____

_____

2. Write a clincher sentence to conclude Paragraph 1. Try to include a transition word or phrase.

_____

_____

_____

3. Write the main idea of Paragraph 2.

_____

_____

_____

4. Write the sentence that destroys the unity of Paragraph 2.

_____

_____

_____

5. Use sensory details to write a sentence that will support the main idea of Paragraph 2.

_____

_____

_____

Paragraph 1

Volcanic eruptions are among the most terrifying and dramatic forces in nature. Lava flows usually burn or bury everything in their path, and the flows can continue for miles and miles. Suffocating ash flows—a mix of hot gases, pumice, rock fragments, and bits of glass—can also accompany an eruption. Debris flows are especially treacherous. Water from lakes or rivers, heavy rain, or melting snow can cause debris on the flanks of a volcano to form into a fast-moving "mudflow" of rock, ash, and cinders. These flows can occur with little warning, and a wall of mud can cover an entire city, claiming thousands of victims before they can react.

Paragraph 2

I remember my favorite classroom quite vividly. The small desks were old and worn, but their wooden tops were sanded, stained dark brown, and polished to a gleaming and smooth work surface. Dark stains bring out the grain of wood better than light stains. A faint smell of chalk dust always pervaded the air, as though someone had just finished clapping erasers together to clean them. The chalkboard was no longer ink black but was instead gray with use and age. The writing on it did not look crisp; rather, it seemed to fade into the gray background.

ELEMENTS OF LANGUAGE | Third Course

That Was Then

My life as a teenager in Colonial America would have been different from my life as a teenager in America today. Although differences would appear in almost every aspect of my life, I will compare the two time periods just in terms of chores, education, and recreation.

For example, the chores I do today are quite different from those I would have done in colonial days. I usually just have to make my bed, keep my room clean, and help clear the table after supper. Sometimes I have to wash the dishes and take out the trash, but not all the time. In colonial days, though, I might have had to get up at sunrise to milk the cows or gather chicken eggs. I also might have had to chop firewood and start a fire before breakfast. Worse yet, I not only would have washed the dishes, but also might have had to haul water from a well before I could wash them! School would also have been different in colonial days. Today I study six different subjects in six different rooms with six different teachers. Back then, I probably would have been in a one-room schoolhouse. One teacher would have taught all subjects and grades, and we probably would have studied reading and writing mostly, without many choices of electives. Other chores I might have had to do include plowing the field, planting crops, or cleaning out the barn.

Similarly, what I would have done for recreation in colonial days is different from what I do now. Today I like to play video games, watch TV, or listen to CDs. Back then, those things wouldn't even have existed. I probably would have run races. Maybe I would have drawn pictures in the dirt with a stick. Teenagers managed to have fun back then even without modern inventions.

6. Write a direct reference that appears in the second paragraph of the passage.

_____

_____

_____

7. Write the sentence where a new paragraph should have begun in this passage.

_____

_____

_____

8. Write the sentence that is out of logical order in this passage.

_____

_____

_____

9. Write an example that could be added to the last paragraph to support the main idea of the paragraph.

_____

_____

_____

10. Write a transition word that will link the last sentence of this passage to preceding sentences.

_____

_____

_____

REVISING A COMPOSITION

DIRECTIONS The following passage needs to be revised. Use what you have learned to improve the passage in the following ways:

- Write a topic sentence to introduce the passage content.
- Write a "clincher" sentence to conclude the passage.
- Mark to show where a new paragraph should begin when a shift in ideas indicates a need for a break.
- Draw a line through the three sentences that are not related to passage content and should be removed.

Toothpaste History

   The development of toothpaste began in the ancient countries of China and India as early as 500 to 300 B.C. Chinese history shows that a learned man named Huang-Ti studied the care of teeth. He claimed that inserting gold and silver needles into different parts of the jaw and gum could cure different types of mouth pain. Theories such as those put forth by Huang-Ti helped lead to the development of dental cream. The ancient Egyptians made a tooth cleaner from a recipe that included powdered ashes of oxen hooves and powdered burnt eggshells. Historians believe that from one million to four million people lived in ancient Egypt. It is likely that the Egyptians used their fingers to rub the mixture onto their teeth. From the records provided by the ancient Chinese, Indians, and Egyptians, the Greeks and Romans also developed and improved toothpaste and advanced dental care. It was the Greeks and Romans who developed a leaden instrument to extract teeth and used wire to hold loose teeth together. The next clear historical references to toothpaste appear in Persian writings around A.D. 1000. The Persians warned about the dangers of using hard toothpowder and advised how to make the best powders. Ancient Persia included parts of what became Iran and Afghanistan. Persian toothpowder included such ingredients as burnt shells of snails and oysters. In the late eighteenth century, toothpowder containing harmful and abrasive ingredients such as brick dust, china, and earthenware became available in Britain. Wealthy individuals applied this powder with brushes, while poorer people used their fingers to rub it on their teeth.

Topic sentence: _____

_____

Clincher sentence: _____

_____

for **CHAPTER 21** page 536

TEST

Reading Workshop: Description of a Place

DIRECTIONS Read the following passage, and answer the questions in the right-hand column.

To Boldly Go . . . to the Supermarket

Modern-day adventurers mistakenly go to the ends of the earth to prove themselves. What they may not realize is that their neighborhood supermarket can also provide a tough testing ground. Survival skills, good reflexes, and a sense of direction like that of the adventurers who scale Mount Everest or explore the Amazon are required.

The first challenge is getting into the store. The expansive surface of supermarket parking lots are treacherous obstacle courses filled with cars, carts, and people. Shoppers are lucky to make it from their parked cars to the entrance. The next difficulty is figuring out which door to use. Many supermarkets present a baffling choice of doors, often marked with contradictory arrows and signs (*Entrance, No Exit, Exit Only, No Entrance, Step Back*). Courageous shoppers must step forward in spite of the danger of being crushed by a swinging automatic door. Next, they must wrestle a cart from a tangle of metal, selecting one without trash or a stuck wheel. Only then may they finally enter the brightly lit world, often larger than several football fields, with its gleaming white linoleum, sweet odors of soap powders and baked goods, and gentle melodies of the store radio station.

Yet more perils await. With the skill of white-water rafters, shoppers navigate the aisles, shelves rising high above them on both sides like the sleek rock faces of a canyon. They cruise past the landmarks of produce, canned and frozen food, dry goods, dairy, meat, soaps, and so on, scanning the landscape for the things they need as well as for unexpected bargains. Always watchful, they avoid obstacles, such as abandoned carts, aisle displays, and employees

1. Which words in this paragraph might be clues to the main idea of the passage?

_____

_____

_____

_____

_____

2. What sensory details does this paragraph include?

_____

_____

_____

_____

3. What three imaginative comparisons are in the third paragraph?

_____

_____

_____

_____

_____

Chapter Tests

who offer free samples of salty crackers and spicy barbecue sauces. Above their heads are the mirrored panels behind which cameras record the shoppers' quests.

At the end of the journey is the checkout. Lighted numbers above the counters signal the weary shoppers. Exhausted, they dock their carts and load their chosen items on an endlessly rotating black rubber ribbon. They consult their watches and wonder if they have set a new record as their groceries are divided among crackling, slippery plastic bags. Finally, their trophies in hand, they head for home, victorious.

4. In the third paragraph, what effect do the words *landscape* and *obstacles* create?

_____
_____
_____
_____
_____

5. What details in the last paragraph might contribute to the article's main idea?

_____
_____
_____
_____
_____

DIRECTIONS Use the ideas and information in the passage you have just read to complete the graphic organizer.

Finding an Implied Main Idea

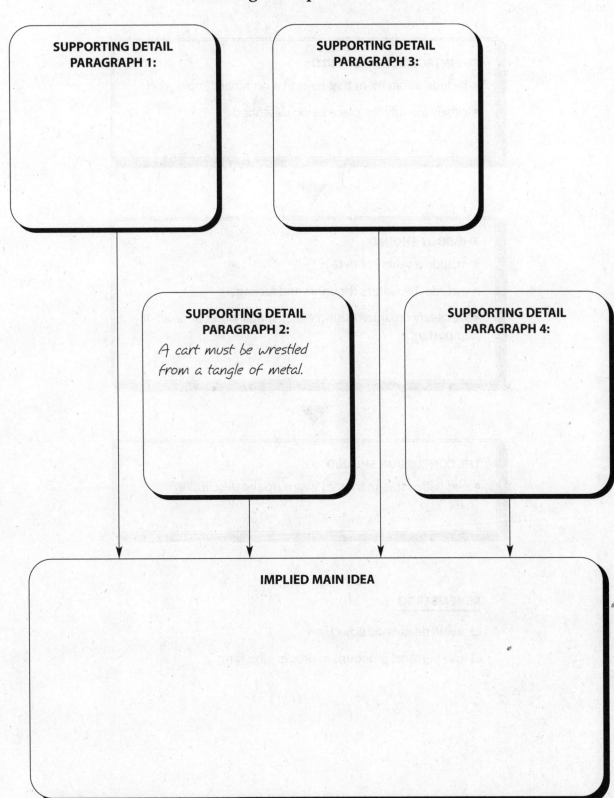

SUPPORTING DETAIL PARAGRAPH 1:

SUPPORTING DETAIL PARAGRAPH 3:

SUPPORTING DETAIL PARAGRAPH 2:

A cart must be wrestled from a tangle of metal.

SUPPORTING DETAIL PARAGRAPH 4:

IMPLIED MAIN IDEA

Writing Workshop: Description of a Place

DIRECTIONS Use the following guidelines to help you revise and correct the description on the next page.

THE INTRODUCTION SHOULD

- include a statement that hints at a dominant impression
- clearly identify the place being described

THE BODY SHOULD

- include a variety of details
- include the writer's thoughts and feelings
- be clearly organized, using either spatial order or order of importance

THE CONCLUSION SHOULD

- end with a statement that wraps up the description

REMEMBER TO

- ❏ avoid deadwood adjectives
- ❏ use personal pronouns in proper case form

Writing Workshop: Revising and Proofreading

DIRECTIONS The following description of a place was written in response to this prompt:

> **Describe your favorite place. Use a variety of details and make sure that you portray your dominant impression of the place.**

The essay contains problems in style, content, organization, and grammar.

- Use the space between the lines for your revisions and corrections.
- If you cannot fit some of your revisions between the lines, rewrite the revised sections on a separate piece of paper.

Ice Dome

I have never lived in a place where there is a real, true winter with snow and ice. The ice rink in my hometown is the closest I have ever been to a cold climate. It is wonderful to escape the cruel, wicked heat of July and walk into winter.

> **a.** Problems with repetitive adjectives

The rink used to be a warehouse. Inside, the skating area itself is 200 feet long and 100 feet wide. The outside is painted baby blue. At the entrance, the name of the rink, Ice Dome, stands out in white. The rink covers about twenty-five thousand square feet.

> **b.** Problem with order

When I was eight, I went to a birthday party there for my friend Alysse. Walking through the double doors, I met Jay, the manager. After giving him three dollars, I stashed my shoes in a locker. A few feet away, I sat on a bench and put on my skates. A mat protected the floor from the blades of my skates. I hobbled over to the rink. Then I launched myself and skated over to Alysse.

> **c.** Problem with sensory details

Her and I then skated arm in arm. Actually, Alysse skated while I
wobbled. When I saw everyone else gliding and spinning on the ice,
I was determined to learn to skate. Meanwhile, I inched my way
around the edge of the rink. When I wasn't catching my balance, I
noticed the powerful exhaust fans in the ceiling, the rows of blue
vinyl seats, the buttery smell of popcorn from the snack bar, the
shrieks of kids slipping on the ice, and the tinny music playing on
the sound system.

When I was younger, the ice rink was my favorite place.

d. Problem with pronoun case

e. Problem with conclusion

Reading Workshop: Personal Narrative

DIRECTIONS Read the following passage, and answer the questions in the right-hand column.

Twister

On our Oklahoma farm, the spring storms of Tornado Alley are a fact of life. Almost every house in our community has a storm cellar, and we discuss weather patterns like professional meteorologists. Tornadoes are always there in the background, waiting to catch us unaware and remind us of what's *really* important in life.

One memorable spring afternoon, a storm approached as my brother Sidney and I completed our chores. We kept an eye on the sky and hurried inside as the wind began to blow in angry gusts.

On the television we saw a line of powerful tornadoes coming. The warnings frightened us, but we still had time to prepare. My brother hurriedly collected flashlights and a battery-powered radio just before the electricity went off. The radio reported a tornado just two minutes away. We made it to the storm cellar in half that time.

There isn't much to do in a dim, damp cellar while you're waiting to see whether your house, barn, livestock, and machinery are blown away. Tense, Sidney and I sat silently, listening to the radio. In the dark, we didn't have to look at each other's worried faces. As the wind howled and the rain pounded, I imagined what a tornado could do to all our hard work. After half an hour, the radio reported that the storm had left the county, so we left the cellar to see what was left of the neighborhood.

We were lucky. We could see that we still had everything— except electricity.

The next morning we ventured out in search of a hot breakfast. As

1. How is the meaning of the experience suggested in the first paragraph?

_____

_____

_____

_____

_____

2. What clues does the narrator provide in the first and second paragraphs to suggest that the farm will survive the storm?

_____

_____

_____

_____

_____

3. From the description in the third paragraph, what predictions can be made about the storm?

_____

_____

_____

_____

_____

we drove to town, I began to see the scope of the storm that had sent us racing to the cellar. Every few miles we'd detour around trees or power lines that blocked the highway. The farther we drove, the more devastation we saw. By the time I got my pancakes, I had mournfully observed the remains of neighbors' houses—houses I knew as well as my own—scattered over their fields. I had seen their heavy farming equipment—expensive, and perhaps not paid for—tied into ribbons or twisted around trees. Lovely old trees were splintered and flung across fences.

By the time the electricity came back on, four days later, we knew how lucky we were to have a house that was dark, but still standing. On the day that we hid in the cellar, forty-three people were killed and more than seventy tornadoes were spotted. When neighbors gathered to help one another clean up, we were all surprisingly cheerful. Lots of *things* had been damaged, but our neighbors had survived. Knowing that an F5 tornado, with winds of three hundred miles per hour, can demolish virtually anything in its path certainly helped the people in my home community adjust their priorities. For me, the tornadoes were a reminder that *family* is the most important part of a family farm.

4. How does the narrator feel about the tornadoes' destruction in this paragraph? Include key words.

_____

_____

_____

_____

_____

5. How does the narrator show the feelings of the people who survived the tornadoes?

_____

_____

_____

_____

_____

DIRECTIONS Complete the graphic organizer, identifying key words that express the writer's personal thoughts and feelings about the experience. Then, describe the thoughts and feelings that are expressed by these words.

Analyzing for Expressive Style

Example

KEY WORD:

worried

Thoughts and feelings expressed by key word:

The narrator feels tense emotions while she sits in the cellar with her brother. She fears the powerful force of the tornadoes and wonders whether the damage will be severe.

KEY WORD:

Thoughts and feelings expressed by key word:

KEY WORD:

Thoughts and feelings expressed by key word:

KEY WORD:

Thoughts and feelings expressed by key word:

Writing Workshop: Personal Narrative

DIRECTIONS Use the following guidelines to help you revise and correct the
personal narrative on the next page.

THE INTRODUCTION SHOULD

- include an attention-grabber
- provide background information
- hint at the meaning of the experience

THE BODY SHOULD

- include details of events, people, and places that make
  them seem real to the reader
- include details about thoughts and feelings
- clearly order the events

THE CONCLUSION SHOULD

- express the meaning of the experience

REMEMBER TO

❑ use precise verbs

❑ use correct subject-verb agreement without being distracted by interrupting
prepositional phrases

Writing Workshop: Revising and Proofreading

DIRECTIONS The following personal narrative was written in response to this prompt:

> **Share an experience in which you volunteered or helped another person.**

The narrative contains problems in organization, style, and usage.

- Use the space between the lines to revise the paper and correct the errors.
- If you cannot fit some of your revisions between the lines, rewrite the revised sections on a separate piece of paper.

Working the Marathon

I find it exciting to attend major sports events. Every year, instead

of just watching an event, I get to be a part of the action by volun-

teering at the New York City Marathon.

a. Problem with introduction

As a volunteer, it's my job to distribute cups of water, to watch

for overexerted athletes, and to cheer on the runners. Last year, I

was assigned to the volunteer post at the 18-mile mark. It's not my

favorite place. I prefer to watch the 30,000 runners take off from

Staten Island, but multiple volunteer posts along the 26.2-mile route

is needed. By the time the runners reached my volunteer post in

Manhattan, they had already run through Staten Island, Brooklyn,

and Queens.

b. Problem with subject-verb agreement

Besides volunteers, innumerable spectators cheer the exhausted

runners. At my post, I saw runners enter Manhattan along First

Avenue. We welcomed them with shouts and announcements over

loudspeakers; bands played everywhere, and residents blasted

music out of their windows.

Chapter Tests

They had almost reached the 20-mile mark, which is called "The
Wall," because runners face overwhelming exhaustion when they
reach this point. At the 18-mile post our duty was to encourage the
individual runners. To make matters worse, most of the runners
would not complete the race for another hour. Some of the runners
wore shirts bearing their names, and I said their names to encourage
them. A man in his eighties received a lot of attention from the
crowd.

c. Problem with order

d. Problem with precise verb

Although the first few runners passed my post within the second
hour of the race, most of them came by in the next five hours. After
most of the runners had passed, I rushed to the finish line in Central
Park to see people complete the final stretch. At this point, many
participants were dazed. I helped direct the runners to a chute at the
finish line and gave participants a medal, a blanket, water, and a
small bag of food. Marathoners call this enforced cool-down the
"death march"—they desperately wanted to stop, but we kept them
walking to help them bring down their heart rate properly. I noticed
that the runners looked tired.

e. Problem with details about thoughts and feelings

The New York City Marathon is a great event for both athletes
and spectators.

f. Problem with conclusion

Reading Workshop: Comparison-Contrast Article

DIRECTIONS Read the following passage, and answer the questions in the right-hand column.

The History of Time

How old are you? When is your next history test? What day does your favorite television show air? You can probably answer these questions automatically, but what if the words to answer them did not exist? Thousands of years ago, the ancient Egyptians recognized the need for a system of measuring time and created many calendars including a solar calendar to mark the cycle of the Nile's floods. This ancient Egyptian calendar was later changed by the Romans and modified by Pope Gregory XIII, but its features can still be found in our modern calendar.

An Egyptian lunar calendar dates back six thousand years. However, a calendar based on the moon's cycles did not accurately reflect the change in seasons. Marking the time for planting was a serious issue for an agricultural society dependent on the Nile's floods to irrigate their fields. The ancient Egyptians reformed their calendar in about 1200 B.C. To develop a solar calendar, ancient Egyptian astronomers calculated the time it takes Earth to circle the sun.

Like our modern calendar, the ancient Egyptian solar calendar divided each year into twelve months, each month into weeks, each week into days and each day into hours. An ancient Egyptian day was a period of twenty-four hours. However, the hours were not a standard length: daylight and darkness were each divided into twelve parts. To adjust for the shorter days and longer nights of winter, the Egyptians simply changed the length of each hour. Whereas the fundamental unit of modern timekeeping is the second, the ancient Egyptians referred to the hour. Unlike our modern

1. What is the main point the writer makes in the first paragraph?

_____

_____

_____

_____

_____

2. Why was it important to the ancient Egyptians to develop a solar calendar?

_____

_____

_____

_____

_____

3. How does the ancient Egyptian day differ from the modern one?

_____

_____

_____

_____

Chapter Tests

calendar, an ancient Egyptian month consisted of three weeks, and a week consisted of ten days.

With only 360 days, the ancient Egyptian calendar still was not accurate. Five days were added to the end of each year and were used to honor the Egyptian deities Osiris, Isis, Horus, Set, and Nephthys. However, because it actually takes the earth 365 and ¼ days to circle the sun, the calendar still was not exactly right. In 238 B.C., a leap year was created, adding one day every four years to make up for the additional ¼ day.

The Romans conquered Egypt in 48 B.C., but they maintained the ancient Egyptian calendar. Julius Caesar instituted it throughout the Roman Republic and gave the months Roman names. However, the Julian calendar still contained slight inaccuracies that accumulated significantly over the centuries. In 1582, Pope Gregory XIII adjusted the Julian calendar by omitting ten days, modifying the method for determining leap years, and moving the extra leap year day to February 29. Although the modern calendar has been modified by both a Roman ruler and a pope, it still reveals its ancient Egyptian roots. The priests and pharaohs who developed a system to predict the Nile's floods would probably recognize their contributions to our calendar today.

4. What is the purpose of the leap year?

_____
_____
_____
_____
_____

5. According to the writer, what is the difference between the ancient Egyptian calendar and the Julian calendar?

_____
_____
_____
_____
_____

DIRECTIONS Use the ideas and information in the essay you have just read to complete the graphic organizer. Fill in the missing details comparing the ancient Egyptian calendar and the modern calendar.

Analyzing Comparison-Contrast Structure

POINTS	SUBJECTS	
	Ancient Egyptian Calendar	**Modern Calendar**
1. division of year	twelve months	twelve months
2. division of month	three weeks	
3. division of week		
4. division of day		
5. smallest unit of time		
6. changes made for accuracy		extra leap year day moved to February 29

Writing Workshop: Comparison-Contrast Essay

DIRECTIONS Use the following guidelines to help you revise and correct the essay on the next page.

THE INTRODUCTION SHOULD

- grab the audience's attention in the first one or two sentences
- provide background information
- clearly identify both subjects in the thesis of the essay

THE BODY SHOULD

- explain each subject and provide supporting details for each feature
- be organized by the block method or the point-by-point method

THE CONCLUSION SHOULD

- bring the essay to a definite close by summarizing or evaluating the subjects

---

REMEMBER TO

- ❑ vary sentence length
- ❑ correct misplaced modifiers

TEST

Writing Workshop: Revising and Proofreading

DIRECTIONS The following comparison-contrast essay was written in response to this prompt:

> **What are the similarities and differences between downhill skiing and cross-country skiing?**

The essay contains problems in style, organization, and grammar.
- Use the space between the lines to revise the paper and correct the errors.
- If you cannot fit some of your revisions between the lines, rewrite the revised sections on a separate piece of paper.

Which Way to Ski?

For many downhill skiers, there is nothing like the moment when they stand at the top of a mountain, viewing the slope below. Facing a gentle slope, the sight exhilarates the beginning skier and the advanced skier eyeing an expert trail. Cross-country skiers may speak of a different thrill—the sense of adventure as they enter a forest blanketed in snow.

a. Problem with introduction

b. Problem with participial phrase

Relatively few people live near downhill ski slopes. Downhill skiers usually have to drive to get to the slopes. They may even have to fly to reach a ski area. However, cross-country skiers can ski wherever there are a few inches of snow.

c. Problem with repetitive sentence length

A financial consideration for most downhill skiers is the price of lift tickets. Many cross-country skiers can ski free of charge. However, for those cross-country skiers who prefer the groomed trails offered at some resorts, trail passes are an expense.

All skiers must rent or purchase the necessary equipment and clothing. However, outfitting a cross-country skier usually costs less than outfitting a downhill skier.

Although cross-country skiing is not completely risk-free, learning to ski on level ground at a walker's pace reduces the possibility of injury. Downhill skiing, however, may not be the best way to start a fitness program. Both types of skiing can provide an excellent workout. Beginning downhill skiers who are not in good physical condition can easily injure themselves. Muscle tone and strength, combined with common sense and a few skiing lessons, are the best means of preventing injury on the downhill slopes. Depending on your level of fitness, cross-country skiing can provide a low-impact exercise, or a high-energy training session.

> **d.** Problem with organization

Regardless of personal preferences, most skiers can agree on some things.

> **e.** Problem with conclusion

Reading Workshop: Cause-and-Effect Article

DIRECTIONS Read the following passage, and answer the questions in the right-hand column.

How Languages Are Lost

Just as civilizations rise and fall, so do the languages that people speak. Ancient Greek and Latin are considered dead languages because no one speaks them outside of the classroom. Many living languages, however, are just barely alive. Around the world, many speakers of rare and ancient languages now choose to communicate in more widely spoken languages. As a result, many linguists fear that the modern world, with its emphasis on global communication and international markets, will bring about a speedy end to the diversity of world languages. When languages die, we lose valuable information about our world and its history.

In a region of South America known as the Peruvian Amazon, many languages have already become extinct. About a hundred and fifty languages were once spoken there. These languages flourished in isolation. However, because of the introduction of modern communication and transportation, only fifty-seven of these languages still existed at the end of the twentieth century. According to linguist Mary Ruth Wise, almost half of those remaining languages are in grave danger of being lost.

In danger of extinction are several Peruvian tribal languages spoken by members of isolated jungle communities. As outsiders came into the jungles of the Amazon, Peruvian tribes, languages, and cultures began to change. When Spanish speakers moved to the region, they established schools in which only Spanish was spoken and brought with them radios that blared news broadcasts in Spanish. The Spanish speakers grew politically and culturally powerful, and Spanish became the dominant language in the region. As a result,

1. How might an emphasis on global communication and international markets bring about the end of certain languages?

_____

_____

_____

_____

_____

2. How did the introduction of the Spanish language affect tribal languages?

_____

_____

_____

_____

_____

speakers of regional tribal languages began to feel that their cultures, customs, and languages were inferior. Over time, these native speakers took up European customs and began to learn and speak Spanish, neglecting their own language.

At the end of the twentieth century, twenty-five Peruvian tribal languages were close to extinction, and the only speakers of these languages were a handful of elderly people. They are likely to be the last native speakers of these languages. Their children and grandchildren prefer Spanish and have no interest in learning the language of their elders. Furthermore, scholars have not fully documented these endangered languages. As elderly speakers die, they take the last memories of their language and culture with them.

Linguists are distressed over the consequences of failing to preserve these languages. With the disappearance of a language, we lose the key that unlocks knowledge of how its speakers lived, worked, thought, and dreamed. It is almost as though those people, their language, and their culture had never existed. Furthermore, the decline in the number of languages spoken in the world points to an ever-narrowing world culture. What will happen as more and more people speak fewer and fewer languages? What will happen if everyone shares the same culture, wears the same clothing, and eats the same food? Our world could become much less interesting.

3. Why will some tribal languages probably die?

_____

_____

_____

_____

_____

4. What happens when languages disappear?

_____

_____

_____

_____

5. Which causal pattern is used in the final paragraph: focus on causes, focus on effects, or causal chain?
Name the cause(s) and effect(s).

_____

_____

_____

_____

DIRECTIONS Use the ideas and information in the fourth paragraph of the passage you have just read to complete the graphic organizer.

Analyzing a Cause-and-Effect Pattern

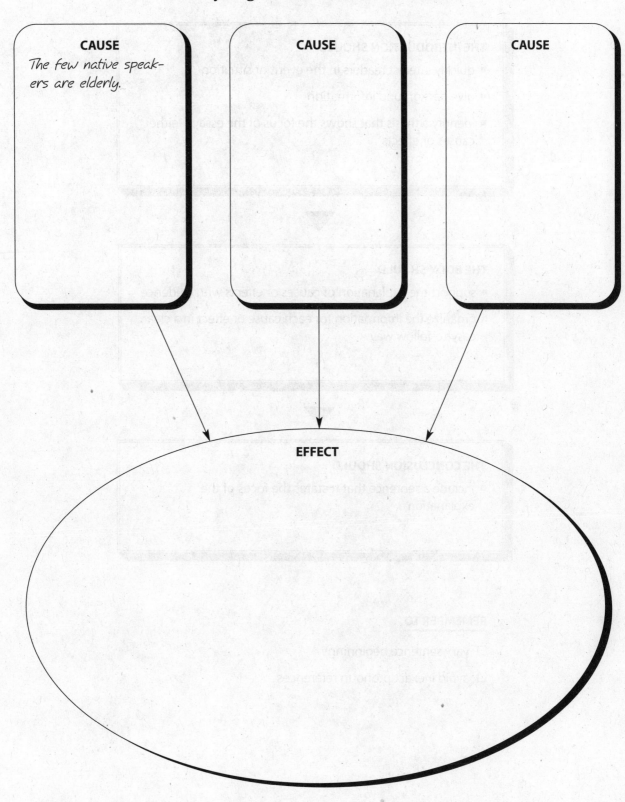

CAUSE

The few native speakers are elderly.

CAUSE

CAUSE

EFFECT

for **CHAPTER 24** | *page 652* | **REVISING GUIDELINES**

Writing Workshop: Cause-and-Effect Explanation

DIRECTIONS Use the following guidelines to help you revise and correct the essay on the next page.

THE INTRODUCTION SHOULD

- quickly interest readers in the event or situation

- give background information

- identify a thesis that shows the focus of the essay—either causes or effects

---

THE BODY SHOULD

- support the explanation of causes or effects with evidence

- organize the information for each cause or effect in a clear, easy-to-follow way

---

THE CONCLUSION SHOULD

- include a sentence that restates the focus of the explanation

---

REMEMBER TO

- ❏ vary sentence beginnings
- ❏ avoid inexact pronoun references

Writing Workshop: Revising and Proofreading

DIRECTIONS The following cause-and-effect essay was written in response to this prompt:

What are the effects of developing good study habits?

The essay contains problems in style, content, organization, and grammar.

- Use the space between the lines to revise the paper and correct the errors.
- If you cannot fit some of your revisions between the lines, rewrite the revised sections on a separate piece of paper.

The Benefits of Studying

When students graduate from middle school, they face many changes. Classes become increasingly more difficult. High school teachers ask students to learn and remember more than they did in middle school. Once students leave eighth grade, they need to study every day to do well in school.

> **a.** Problem with inexact pronoun reference

Studying regularly helps students perform better on tests. However, students who study for several days before the test tend to score even higher than those who study only the night before the test. If students study the night before a test, they remember information better than students who do not study at all.

> **b.** Problem with organization in this paragraph

However, teachers grade students on more than just tests. Students need to study for these things, too.

> **c.** Problem with supporting evidence

Students who study regularly also feel more confident. These students don't have to worry about doing work at the last minute. These students don't feel uneasy in class. These students don't feel left out of class discussions.

> **d.** Problem with sentence beginnings

In addition, students who study every night often discover

that they become more interested in class and in the subject. They

develop new ideas and connect what they study to their personal

lives.

High school is hard work.

e. Problem with conclusion

Reading Workshop: Analysis of a Poem

DIRECTIONS Read the poem and the following passage, and answer
the questions in the right-hand column.

My Papa's Waltz

The whiskey on your breath
Could make a small boy dizzy;
But I hung on like death:
Such waltzing was not easy.

We romped until the pans
Slid from the kitchen shelf;
My mother's countenance
Could not unfrown itself.

The hand that held my wrist
Was battered on one knuckle;
At every step you missed
My right ear scraped a buckle.

You beat time on my head
With a palm caked hard by dirt,
Then waltzed me off to bed
Still clinging to your shirt.

—Theodore Roethke

"Such Waltzing Was Not Easy"

The emotional truths of Theodore Roethke's poem "My Papa's
Waltz" lie in its central image of a clumsy, breathtaking dance. This
waltz becomes a metaphor for the complicated relationship of son
and father. The traditional waltz is steady, rhythmic, and predictable. As the poem progresses, rhythm is broken and steps are
missed. The significance of the details unfolds stanza by stanza in a
series of concrete images. The poem expresses in simple language a
complicated mixture of love and longing.

Roethke sets the tone with these blunt lines in the opening
stanza: "The whiskey on your breath / Could make a small boy
dizzy; / But I hung on like death." The strong smell of alcohol does
not discourage the boy. His need for fatherly attention is almost
desperate: He hangs on "like death." The last line, "Such waltzing
was not easy," sums up the poem.

1. According to the first paragraph, what is the central
image of the poem? Why
do you think the writer
mentions it here?

_____

_____

_____

_____

2. What does the writer infer
about the boy from the
tight grip with which he
holds his father?

_____

_____

_____

_____

_____

"My Papa's Waltz" and excerpts from *The Collected Poems of Theodore
Roethke*. Copyright 1942 by Hearst Magazines, Inc. Reprinted by permission of **Doubleday, a division of Random House, Inc.**

The mother's frowning face in the second stanza shows her disapproval, but the reader is left to guess whether the frown is related to the pans sliding "from the kitchen shelf," to this "romping," or to the father's drinking. The formal word *countenance* breaks the poem's regular *abab* pattern. The rhythm stumbles as if the boy misses a step when he sees his mother's disapproval. The contrast between the drunken, dancing father and the sober, disapproving mother adds to the poem's contradictions.

The rhythm resumes in the third stanza, where we see that the father is holding not the boy's hand but his wrist, a grasp that is difficult to escape. Each dancer is hanging onto the other. The speaker relates, with perhaps a slight complaint in his voice, that "At every step you missed / My right ear scraped a buckle." While the boy remains determined to hang on, the reader may sense his longing for his father to be more mindful of him.

In the third stanza, the physical details of the father's hands— "battered on one knuckle"—continue into the fourth with "a palm caked hard by dirt." Whether these imperfections are remembered tenderly by the speaker is unclear. Does he see his father as a rugged, dirty man who plays too roughly or as a hardworking man who, despite his drinking, enjoys moments of playful tenderness? What *is* clear is that the boy does not want to let go. Although his head must ache from the rhythmic beats of his father's hand, he does not want the dance to end. The image of him clinging to his father's shirt while being taken to bed reveals the child's deep need for love and affection and suggests that his needs are not entirely satisfied.

Without using abstract words like *love, loss,* or *pain,* Roethke uses the simple images of the poem to convey a boy's deep love for his father and the longing and conflicts that often accompany love.

3. According to the writer, what is the effect of the mother's frown?

_____
_____
_____
_____

4. How does the writer support the idea that the boy wishes his father were more careful of him?

_____
_____
_____
_____
_____

5. What does the writer conclude about the speaker's feelings toward his father?

_____
_____
_____
_____
_____

DIRECTIONS Use the ideas and information in the passage you have just read to complete the graphic organizer.

Analyzing Textual Evidence as Support

DIRECT QUOTATION	WHAT IDEA DOES IT SUPPORT?	HOW DOES THE ESSAY ELABORATE?
"The whiskey on your breath / Could make a small boy dizzy; / But I hung on like death"		The essay explains that the smell of alcohol does not discourage the boy and emphasizes that the boy desperately craves his father's attention.
"At every step you missed / My right ear scraped a buckle"	The father is careless of the boy.	
"battered on one knuckle" "a palm caked hard by dirt"		

Writing Workshop: Analysis of a Poem

DIRECTIONS Use the following guidelines to help you revise and correct the essay on the next page.

THE INTRODUCTION SHOULD

- relate the poem's meaning to a common, human experience
- name the author and title
- have a clear thesis
- introduce key poetic elements

THE BODY PARAGRAPHS SHOULD

- provide support and elaboration for each key poetic element
- each have a main idea that is clear and supports the thesis

THE CONCLUSION SHOULD

- effectively remind the readers of the thesis
- bring the essay to a close

REMEMBER TO

❑ revise wordy sentences

❑ punctuate quotations properly

Writing Workshop: Revising and Proofreading

DIRECTIONS The following essay was written in response to this poem:

Mabel Osborne

Your red blossoms amid green leaves
Are drooping, beautiful geranium!
But you do not ask for water.
You cannot speak! You do not need to speak—
Everyone knows that you are dying of thirst,
Yet they do not bring water!
They pass on, saying:
"The geranium wants water."
And I, who had happiness to share
And longed to share your happiness;
I who loved you, Spoon River,
And craved your love,
Withered before your eyes, Spoon River—
Thirsting, thirsting,
Voiceless from chasteness of soul to ask you for love,
You who knew and saw me perish before you,
Like this geranium which someone has planted over me,
And left to die.

                                                   —Edgar Lee Masters

The essay contains problems in style, content, and punctuation.

- Use the space between the lines for your revisions and corrections.
- If you cannot fit some of your revisions between the lines, rewrite the revised sections on a separate piece of paper.

A Voice from the Grave

The speaker in this poem lies underground, like all the speakers

in this collection of poems, *Spoon River Anthology*. They speak from

the cemetery of the fictional town Spoon River, and their words

are meant for those who stroll past their graves. Mabel Osborne

voices the pain of loneliness that everyone experiences at one time

or another. Through addressing first the geranium and then the

reader, through repeating certain words and images, and through

> **a.** Problem with introduction

using a dying geranium as a metaphor for her life, the speaker

expresses the neglect she felt in life.

In the first lines, where the speaker addresses the geranium, the

reader might think that the poem is going to be about her sympathy

for the dying plant. The speaker's voice is gentle, even when she

switches from addressing the geranium to addressing the people of

Spoon River in the line "And I, who had happiness to share." Her

gentleness, however, turns into accusation: "You who knew and saw

me perish before you." In other words, she feels that the citizens of

Spoon River knew what she needed and deliberately withheld it.

The reader is jolted into realizing that this poem is not a poem that

b. Problem with
wordiness

is about a plant that is dying. Instead, it is a cry of pain from a

woman whose death may have been prevented by the very people

passing by her tombstone.

The repetition of key words such as *thirsting, ask,* and *love* reveal

the theme of a deep, basic need that was not met. The repetition of

water indicates the nourishment that she so desperately wanted:

"But you do not ask for water," "Yet they do not bring water", and

c. Problem with
punctuation

The geranium wants water."

The dying plant on Mabel Osborne's grave represents her own

d. Problem with support
and elaboration

life in several ways.

This poem uses poetic devices to communicate the intense pain

e. Problem with conclusion

of a solitary life.

Reading Workshop: Investigative Report

DIRECTIONS Read the following passage, and answer the questions in the right-hand column.

The Right Home for the Right Dog

Last week while I was shopping at a local mall, I saw a group of people with greyhounds on leashes standing in front of a pet store. My family has been talking about getting a dog, so I stopped to look. The greyhounds were retired racing dogs, and their owners were promoting the idea that retired greyhounds should be adopted rather than destroyed. The idea appealed to me immediately. However, since I knew almost nothing about the breed, I needed to determine whether a retired greyhound would be right for our family.

The group gave me a brochure with some general information on greyhounds. I learned that they stand 26 to 29 inches tall at the shoulder and weigh up to 80 pounds. Yet, in spite of their large size, they are considered too gentle to be good watchdogs. The brochure further explains that while greyhounds are bred for speed and can sprint up to 45 miles per hour, they don't necessarily need long daily runs. Playtime in a fenced yard plus three or four long walks each week provide enough exercise. The brochure also recommends that families with children under the age of three not adopt the dogs. Since my youngest daughter is two, I realized that I needed more information.

An Internet search turned up many helpful sites. On one, I found a journal article describing the potential behavior problems of this breed. The article explains that the transition from competitive racer to family pet is not always smooth. For example, because the dogs have been subjected to a rigid schedule, they tend to fear the unfamiliar. It suggests ways for a busy family to provide a regular daily

1. What specific question does the writer set out to answer?

_____

_____

_____

_____

_____

2. What types of sources has the writer used in the second and third paragraphs?

_____

_____

_____

_____

_____

3. What causes the writer to worry about adopting a greyhound?

_____

_____

_____

_____

_____

routine for a greyhound. The article addresses most of my remaining concerns by providing common-sense suggestions for ways to correct unwanted behaviors.

To learn more, I decided to speak with a professional. I called Dr. O'Hanlin, a local veterinarian who works with the greyhound rescue group. Dr. O'Hanlin agreed with what I had learned so far. He said that a fenced backyard does make a good play area, but these dogs should stay indoors in extreme weather. Their short hair, thin skin, and low body fat make them unable to tolerate either extreme heat or extreme cold. Dr. O'Hanlin explained what the initial fee for adopting a greyhound would be and that the fee included an initial checkup and vaccinations. The whole cost of adopting a greyhound would be less than that of buying a purebred puppy.

At this point, my family is excited about rescuing one of these dogs. However, before we make our final decision, we are going to speak directly to some families who have adopted greyhounds and ask them about their experiences. (The greyhound adoption group has given us a list of families.) After talking to them, we will be prepared to make a well-informed decision about whether adopting a greyhound is right for us.

4. What does the writer learn about greyhounds from talking to a veterinarian?

_____

_____

_____

_____

5. What other sources does the writer plan to use before making a final decision? Are they primary or secondary? Explain your answer.

_____

_____

_____

_____

_____

DIRECTIONS Complete the graphic organizer below, summarizing the main idea and supporting details in the report you have just read.

Summarizing What You Read

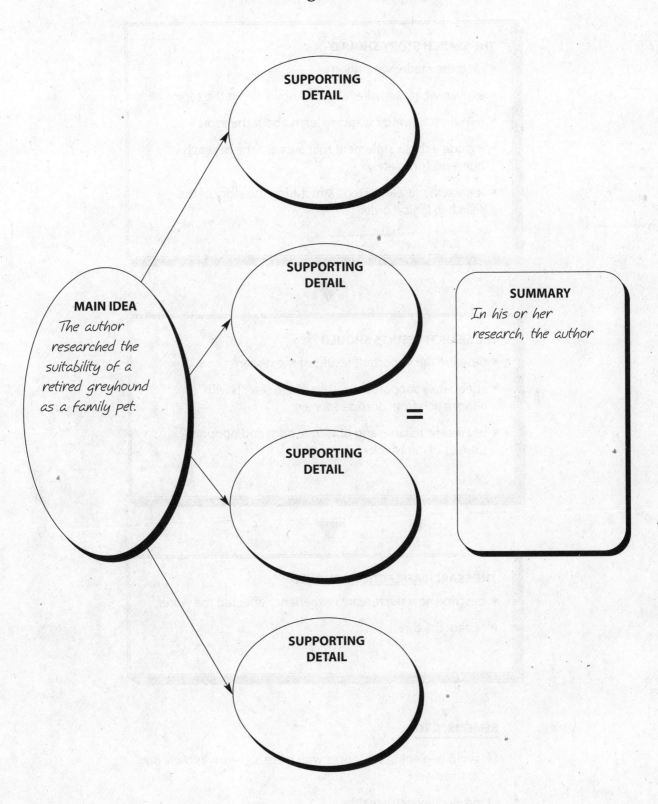

SUPPORTING DETAIL

SUPPORTING DETAIL

MAIN IDEA
The author researched the suitability of a retired greyhound as a family pet.

SUPPORTING DETAIL

SUPPORTING DETAIL

=

SUMMARY
In his or her research, the author

Writing Workshop: I-Search Paper

DIRECTIONS Use the following guidelines to help you revise and correct the
I-Search paper on the next page.

THE SEARCH <u>STORY</u> SHOULD

- grab the reader's attention

- explain what the writer already knows about the topic

- tell what the writer wants to learn about the topic

- include a thesis statement that answers the research
  question completely

- retrace the research steps, structuring the story of the
  search in logical order

THE SEARCH <u>RESULTS</u> SHOULD

- describe the important results of the research

- adequately support the results of the search with
  information from outside sources

- use recent, reliable, and objective print and nonprint
  sources of information

THE SEARCH <u>REFLECTIONS</u> SHOULD

- describe how the research experience affected the writer

- restate the thesis

REMEMBER TO

- ❑ avoid beginning sentences with *there is, there was, there are,*
  or *there were*

- ❑ properly punctuate titles

94

Writing Workshop: Revising and Proofreading

DIRECTIONS The following I-Search paper was written in response to this prompt:

Research a place you would like to visit, and tell the story of your search.

The essay contains problems in style, content, organization, and punctuation.

- Use the space between the lines for your revisions and corrections.
- If you cannot fit some of your revisions between the lines, rewrite the revised sections on a separate piece of paper.

To Conquer France

My two years in French class and my teacher's unforgettable

photos and stories of her student days in France made me eager to

visit that country. I began to wonder what it would take to get there.

> **a.** Problem with introduction

I already knew that France is an important center of art, litera-

ture, and architecture. There are also many impressive ruins, which I

would love to see in person. There is also the delicious food that

France is famous for.

> **b.** Problem with style

I had many questions about how I could spend a summer in

France as a high school student. From all of these questions, I con-

structed my research question: *Is visiting France a realistic goal for me?*

From my search I learned a great deal about the subject.

> **c.** Problem with thesis statement

I decided to ask my French teacher for her advice. She gave me

the name and phone number of a former student who had lived in

> **d.** Problem with organization

France for a year. The student, Jackie Fonza, told me about several

publications that describe affordable ways for students to spend

time in France. Better yet, she told me about student programs for summer language study. My Internet search turned up only very

general information for tourists and students (Yahoo!). I began my

search by skimming through several travel guides in our city library,

but none of them was written for a student who had little money

to spend.

One book Jackie recommended, Let's Go: France, listed volunteer

and work-abroad programs. I will not be eligible for most volunteer

programs until after I graduate.

e. Problem with title

I also learned that a trip could be more affordable than I had

guessed. The only money required for the volunteer programs is

round-trip airfare, which is often half price between October and

May, plus a small weekly fee for meals and housing (Bensson 80).

I learned that France really is a possibility for me if I join a lan-

guage study, volunteer, or work-abroad program. In addition, I met

an interesting person, Jackie, and picked up a lot of information

about France. I'm excited. Whether I go soon or in a few years, this

dream is going to become a reality.

Works Cited

Bensson, Anne, ed. Let's Go: France. New York: St. Martin's Press, 2007.

Fonza, Jackie. Personal interview. 5 June 2008.

Yahoo! 3 Mar. 2008 <http://travel.yahoo.com/p-travelguide-

191501733-france>.

TEST

Reading Workshop: Opinion Piece

DIRECTIONS Read the following passage, and answer the questions in the right-hand column.

Being Young Is Not a Crime
Editorial

Recently, our city council proposed a youth curfew that would prohibit all minors under seventeen years of age from frequenting streets, business establishments, or "places of assembly" after 11:00 P.M. Such a curfew not only strips both youth and their parents of their rights, it also assumes that an entire group of people are suspect just because they are under seventeen years of age.

No legal precedent has been set for curfews in the U.S. The Supreme Court denied a request to review a case, and the lower courts have given conflicting verdicts on other cases. This means that our city council does not have the right to enact this proposal.

Supporters of the proposal have said that children shouldn't be out at 3:00 A.M. Who *should* be out at 3:00 A.M.? The point is that everyone has the *right* to travel as he or she pleases, even at 3:00 A.M. The First Amendment, which states that "Congress shall make no law respecting . . . the right of the people peaceably to assemble," clearly entitles all Americans to convene in public places, regardless of the hour. Despite the common misperception that these rights do not apply to minors, it was ruled in *Tinker v. Des Moines* that youths have full First Amendment rights.

On the other hand, parents and guardians are entitled to control their children's behavior in many ways. For example, parents have the right to stipulate when their underage children can secure a driver's license. In fact, in some states the parent or legal guardian of a minor must sign the child's license application. This brings us to another point: A youth curfew not only infringes on the rights of

1. What is the writer's purpose?

_____

_____

_____

_____

2. What persuasive words or phrases does the writer use in the first paragraph to appeal to the readers' emotions?

_____

_____

_____

_____

3. What logical appeals are used in the third paragraph?

_____

_____

_____

_____

minors, it also usurps the rights of parents. After all, who knows our youth better? Their families or the city council?

If the proposal passes the city council at the next meeting, minors will no longer be allowed to attend midnight mass, study for midterms at the late-night coffee shop, or attend evening outdoor concerts at Stevenson Park. In fact, after a certain hour, minors won't even be allowed to walk around their own block. This proposal must be stopped. It is unprecedented, unconstitutional, and intrusive on parental rights. Please attend next Tuesday's city council meeting at city hall at 7:00 P.M., and speak out. Let the council members know that our city's youth are citizens, too.

4. What types of appeals are provided as support in the fourth paragraph?

_____

_____

_____

_____

_____

5. What is the writer asking people to do?

_____

_____

_____

_____

_____

DIRECTIONS Use the ideas and information in the passage you have just read to complete the graphic organizer. Cite a fact or example from the text to support each reason. Label each fact or example as such.

Recognizing Logical Appeals

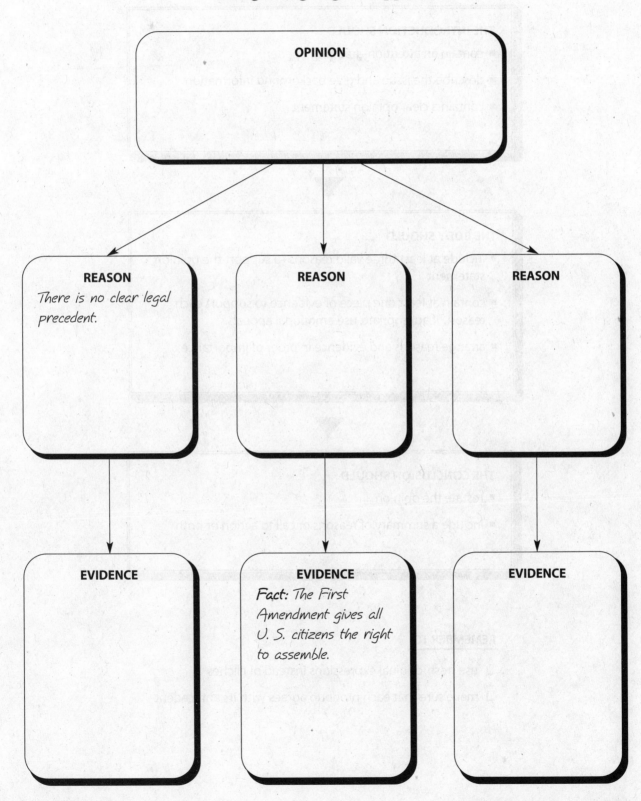

OPINION

REASON
There is no clear legal precedent.

REASON

REASON

EVIDENCE

EVIDENCE
Fact: The First Amendment gives all U. S. citizens the right to assemble.

EVIDENCE

Writing Workshop: Persuasive Paper

DIRECTIONS Use the following guidelines to help you revise and correct the essay on the next page.

THE INTRODUCTION SHOULD

- contain an attention-grabbing opener

- describe the issue and give background information

- contain a clear opinion statement

THE BODY SHOULD

- include at least three valid reasons to support the opinion statement

- contain at least one piece of evidence to support each reason. If appropriate, use emotional appeals.

- arrange reasons and evidence in order of importance

THE CONCLUSION SHOULD

- restate the opinion

- include a summary of reasons or call to action or both

REMEMBER TO

❑ use fresh, original expressions instead of clichés

❑ make sure that each pronoun agrees with its antecedent

Writing Workshop: Revising and Proofreading

DIRECTIONS The following persuasive essay was written in response to this prompt:

> **State and support an opinion regarding part-time employment of students.**

The essay contains problems in content, usage, grammar, and style.

- Use the space between the lines to revise the paper and correct the errors.
- If you cannot fit some of your revisions between the lines, rewrite the revised sections on a separate piece of paper.

Part-time Employment Hurts Students

Although many students are tempted to find part-time jobs, this could be a mistake. Work disrupts a student's education and ability to explore interests and activities.

| **a.** Problem with introduction |

Education requires a full-time commitment from students. Not only do they attend classes for most of the day, they must also spend hours outside of school studying. A part-time job competes with school, distracting students from their schoolwork. Each student who works risks falling asleep in their classes. Students who work are more likely to fall behind and get poor grades.

| **b.** Problem with agreement |

Although a part-time job can be a way to learn more about the world and experience financial independence, it may be wise for students to postpone getting a job. A part-time job prevents young people from learning about other valuable aspects of life. After all, life is what you make it.

| **c.** Problem with cliché |

The added stress of a part-time job can have a negative effect on

students' health and even their personalities.

> **d.** Problem with support

Young people should avoid part-time work to focus on getting

an education, a full-time job in itself. A part-time job interferes with

students' lives.

> **e.** Problem with
> conclusion

Reading Workshop: Critical Review

DIRECTIONS Read the following passage, and answer the questions in the right-hand column.

Frasier: **A Cultured Comedy**

What made the situation comedy *Frasier* such a success? It was not the typical sitcom that television programmers usually count on for wide mass appeal. Nevertheless, its large audience consisted of ordinary viewers and critics alike. With its superb acting, witty dialogue, and complex characters, this show found its way to the top of the sitcom competition when it originally aired.

A show can succeed or fail simply on the quality of its acting. *Frasier* was one of those rare shows that was loaded with first-rate talent. Kelsey Grammer won Emmy awards for his title role as Dr. Frasier Crane, a psychiatrist with his own radio talk show. David Hyde Pierce, who played Frasier's snobbish, competitive brother Niles, also received Emmys for his role in the series. Emmy nominee Jane Leeves played Daphne, a home-care provider. John Mahoney as the ex-cop father and Peri Gilpin as a radio show producer completed an outstanding cast.

In general, intelligent dialogue has not been an outstanding characteristic of situation comedy. The script of *Frasier,* however, combines witty banter with sometimes obscure cultural references, and viewers still love it in reruns. Niles and Frasier discuss art and opera, pepper their conversation with French phrases, and show off their vocabulary. The contrast of their education and lifestyle with their petty sibling rivalry is a source of the show's humor.

The characters themselves embody the contrast between external knowledge and self-knowledge. They are complex and fascinating and remind us of our own flaws. The brothers' constant need to outdo each other professionally, intellectually, and socially, along

1. According to the first paragraph, what criteria will this critic use to judge the show?

_____
_____
_____
_____
_____

2. Why do you think the information in the second paragraph has been included?

_____
_____
_____
_____

3. Identify one fact in the third paragraph. How could it be proven or confirmed?

_____
_____
_____
_____
_____

with their endearing ignorance of their motives, undermines their professionalism. Their knowledge of psychiatry and their ability to help solve their clients' problems do not seem to carry over into their own lives and, in fact, lead them into trouble. As the brothers incessantly analyze every event, situation, and relationship in their lives, they make a mess of every one. They use their psychological explanations to excuse their inconsistencies and thus avoid confronting their faults.

The characterization does have flaws. The characters seem never to change, and their peculiarities are often exaggerated to the point of being grating. The contrast between the brothers and their father is amusing. Their snobbery and his stubbornness, however, are taken to extremes and often seem unrealistic. The show became predictable as the same conflicts appeared from week to week.

Do the show's virtues outweigh its drawbacks? For this reviewer, the answer is a definite yes. The award-winning cast, intelligent dialogue, and complex characterizations combined to make *Frasier* one of the best situation comedies of all time.

4. What evaluation criterion does the critic focus on in the fourth paragraph?

_____

_____

_____

_____

5. Identify an opinion in the last paragraph. Explain your answer.

_____

_____

_____

_____

_____

DIRECTIONS Use the ideas and information in the passage you have just read to complete the graphic organizer. Be sure to include both positive and negative statements where these apply.

Recognizing Evaluation Criteria

► CRITERIA USED TO RATE THE SHOW	► STATEMENTS SHOWING HOW THE SHOW RATES BY THE CRITERIA
	"Frasier was one of those rare shows that was loaded with first-rate talent."

Writing Workshop: Critical Review

DIRECTIONS Use the following guidelines to help you revise and correct the review on the next page.

THE INTRODUCTION SHOULD

- grab the reader's attention
- give basic background information
- include a thesis that states the writer's opinion of the show with a brief list of reasons for that opinion

EACH BODY PARAGRAPH SHOULD

- present a reason for the writer's opinion
- provide support for the reason in the form of observations and examples

THE CONCLUSION SHOULD

- restate the writer's opinion
- offer viewers a recommendation

REMEMBER TO

- ❑ avoid using the same sentence patterns again and again
- ❑ use adverb clauses to combine closely related simple sentences
- ❑ correct run-on sentences

Writing Workshop: Revising and Proofreading

DIRECTIONS The following critical review was written in response to this prompt:

> **Write a short review of a television situation comedy.**

The review contains problems in content, style, and grammar.

- Use the space between the lines to revise the paper and correct the errors.
- If you cannot fit some of your revisions between the lines, rewrite the revised sections on a separate piece of paper.

3rd Rock from the Sun Is Silliness at Its Best

These people are literally from outer space. The situation

comedy *3rd Rock from the Sun* is one of the funniest shows ever

made for television.

> **a.** Problem with statement of opinion and reasons

The plot of the show involves a group of aliens spending some

time as human beings on a planet they consider one of the least

important. (The "3rd Rock" is Earth.) They join middle-class

> **b.** Problem with run-on sentences

American existence as the Solomons, an extended family made up

of the leader Dick, his sister Sally, his brother Harry, and his son

Tommy, each hilarious episode deals with the Solomons' attempts to

fit in with the people around them and appear normal. Because the

characters are different ages, they deal with different people and

have different kinds of problems. Another thing that keeps the plot

interesting and suspenseful is the possibility that they could be

ordered to leave Earth at any time. Some of the time they're afraid

they'll have to leave, at other times, they just want to go back home

and escape the craziness of Earth.

The humor of the show is its best quality. The family hears that a baby has its mother's eyes. They panic. They worry terribly about the mother. There are a lot of possibilities for humor in that kind of figure of speech. At times, the humor has a serious side. It makes you question how you assume people should behave. For example, Dick can't catch on that a man isn't expected to show his feelings.

> **c.** Problem with sentence style

The actors of *3rd Rock* were really responsible for making this show work. John Lithgow's performance as Dick stands out. He is hilarious as he innocently and constantly upsets the woman he is in love with. All the actors have great comic timing. They throw themselves into the plot with a lot of energy. None of the characters are weird, except maybe Dick. The rest of the family—Sally (Kristen Johnston), Harry (French Stewart), and Tommy (Joseph Gordon-Levitt)—are really cool and self-confident.

With such an entertaining story line, absurd humor, and great comic actors, *3rd Rock* has a lot to offer. It's witty and zany, but it reminds us that we don't always understand everything about our own culture.

> **d.** Problem with recommendation